natural English

elementary workbook with key
Carol Tabor

OXFORD

contents

2

one

Tick (✓) when you've done these sections.

natural English
- [ ] saying hello
- [ ] *How are you?*
- [ ] *Would you like …?*
- [ ] asking for help

grammar
- [ ] *be* positive and negative
- [ ] *a / an*
- [ ] questions with *be*
- [ ] expand your grammar *the* with place names

vocabulary
- [ ] jobs
- [ ] numbers (1)
- [ ] countries and nationalities
- [ ] drinks
- [ ] expand your vocabulary containers

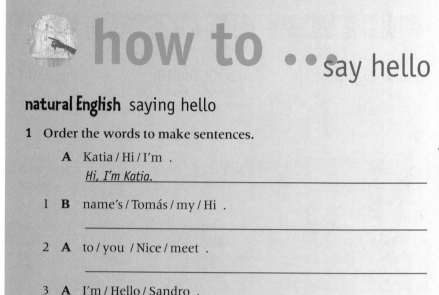

how to …say hello

natural English saying hello

1 Order the words to make sentences.

> **A** Katia / Hi / I'm .
> *Hi, I'm Katia.*

1 **B** name's / Tomás / my / Hi .
_____

2 **A** to / you / Nice / meet .
_____

3 **A** I'm / Hello / Sandro .
_____

4 **B** Hello / Rebecca / my / name's .
_____

5 **A** meet / to / Rebecca / Nice / you .
_____

grammar *be* positive and negative

2 Are sentences 1 to 8 true ✓ or false ✗?

> Tomás is a teacher. ✓
1 Katia is from Barcelona.
2 Katia isn't married.
3 Tomás is from Poland.
4 Tomás is single.
5 Katia isn't a doctor.
6 Tomás is from Spain.
7 Tomás isn't forty.
8 Katia is thirty.

Katia

Tomás

SPAIN

●Barcelona

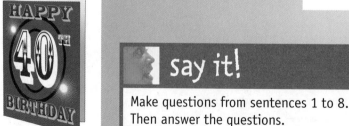

say it!

Make questions from sentences 1 to 8.
Then answer the questions.

> Is Tomás a teacher?

> Yes, he is.

vocabulary jobs

3 Look at the pictures and complete the puzzle. Find one more job.

A C T O R

grammar a/an

4 Complete the sentences with a/an.

Sue's _a_ businesswoman.

1 Lana's _____ office worker.
2 Marco is _____ police officer.
3 I'm _____ housewife.
4 He's _____ actor.
5 She's _____ engineer.

wordbooster

numbers (1)

5 Write the numbers for each picture.

1 _thirty-two_ _____ pence
2 _____
3 _____
4 _____
5 _____
6 _____ dollars

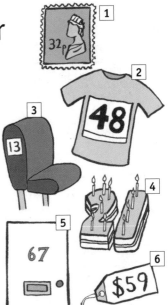

say it!

Say the numbers.

| your telephone or mobile phone number | your classroom number |
| your house or flat number | your age |

countries and nationalities

think back!

Remember two countries in Asia, Europe, and South America.

6 Complete the sentences. Use nationalities and the correct form of be.

Juan's from Spain. He _'s Spanish_ .

1 Ragini's from Thailand. She _____ .
2 Heidi and Hans are from Germany. They _____ .
3 Simone's from France. She _____ .
4 Yuki's from Japan. He _____ .
5 Ana and Feliks are from Poland. They _____ .
6 Marina's from Argentina. She _____ .
7 Emiliano's from Italy. He _____ .
8 Min and Chao are from China. They _____ .

expand your grammar

the /(–) with place names

Use *the* with names which include:

kingdom   islands   states   republic

<u>the</u> Balearic Islands

<u>the</u> Dominican Republic

<u>the</u> Kingdom of Saudi Arabia

Add *the* or (–) to the places. Use a dictionary to check new words.

	<u>*the*</u>	Madeira Islands
1	_____	United States of America (USA)
2	_____	China
3	_____	Australia
4	_____	United Kingdom (UK)
5	_____	Canary Islands
6	_____	Hungary
7	_____	Brazil
8	_____	Czech Republic

Tick ✓ or correct the sentences.

     the
Sam is from ∧Balearic Islands.
My office is in Colombia. ✓

1 Budapest is in the Hungary.
2 Rick is from United States.
3 Helen is a student in Australia.
4 My teacher is from China.
5 London is in United Kingdom.

questions questions

questions

natural English *How are you?*

7 Complete the dialogue.

Paul   <u>*Hi*</u> _____ Gemma, ¹_____ are you?

Gemma   ²_____ thanks. And ³_____?

Paul   ⁴_____ well, ⁵_____.

grammar questions with *be*

8 Match the questions and answers.

Is he from China?	a Mary.
1 Where is the Eiffel Tower?	b Fine, thanks.
2 What's his phone number?	c No, I'm not.
3 Are you in the elementary class?	d No, they aren't.
4 Are they married?	e 01981 6768 5910.
5 How are you?	f No, he's married.
6 Is she a new student?	g Yes, he is.
7 Who's your teacher?	h Yes, she is.
8 Is he single?	i It's in Paris.

vocabulary drinks

9 Complete the phrases. Use the words in the box.

black   orange   red   diet   mineral   ~~hot~~

	<u>*hot*</u>	chocolate
1	_____	juice
2	_____	cola
3	_____	water
4	_____	wine
5	_____	coffee

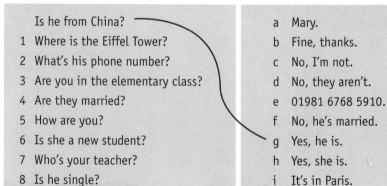

natural English *Would you like ...?*

10 Order the words and complete the dialogues.

A a / drink / Would / like / you ?

Would you like a drink?

B Yes, please.

1 **A** you / like / glass / wine / Would / a / of ?

_____

B No, thanks.

2 **A** like / you / tea / lemon / Would / with ?

_____

B Yes, please.

3 **A** Would you like a drink?

B diet / Yes / cola / a / please .

_____

4 **A** like / hot / a / Would / chocolate / you ?

_____

B No, thanks.

5 **A** Would you like a drink ?

B a / water / please / Yes / mineral .

_____

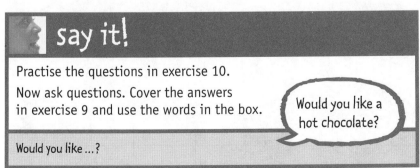

say it!

Practise the questions in exercise 10.

Now ask questions. Cover the answers in exercise 9 and use the words in the box.

> Would you like a hot chocolate?

Would you like ...?

containers

What is in each container? Tick ✓ the boxes.

		coffee	wine	fruit juice	cola	hot chocolate
glass			✓	✓	✓	
1 bottle						
2 can						
3 mug						
4 carton						
5 cup						

Underline the best word.

Would you like a <u>cup</u> / carton of coffee?

1 A mug / glass of red wine, please.

2 Two bottles / cups of cola.

3 A cup / carton of orange juice.

4 Would you like a glass / mug of hot chocolate?

5 Two cans / cups of diet cola, please.

pronunciation sounds

abcdefghijklm
nopqrstuvwxyz

11 Add letters with the same sound to the circles.

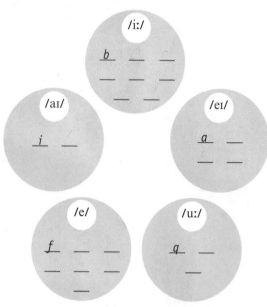

/iː/
b _ _ _
_ _ _

/aɪ/
i _

/eɪ/
a _
_ _

/e/
f _ _
_ _
_

/uː/
q _
_

What two letters are not in the circles?

think back!

Cover the circles. Say the letters with the same sound as *a*, *b*, *f*, *i*, and *q*.

say it!

Spell the words.

your name
your job
your country
your nationality
your age

A – n – g – e – l – a

write it!

Write the words from the exercise above.

natural English asking for help

12 Write a or b.

a   Sorry, can you repeat that, please?
b   Sorry, can you play that again, please?

two

Tick (✓) when you've done these sections.

natural English
- [ ] *thing(s)*
- [ ] giving opinions
- [ ] *Can I …? / Can you …?*
- [ ] saying you aren't sure

grammar
- [ ] *have got* (= have)
- [ ] possessive *'s*
- [ ] *this, that, these, those*
- [ ] expand your grammar plural nouns

vocabulary
- [ ] technology
- [ ] personal things
- [ ] adjectives (1)
- [ ] expand your vocabulary in the office

have you got one?

vocabulary technology

1 Look at pictures 1 to 5 and find the words for these things in the puzzle. Which word is not in the puzzle?

M	B	Y	L	C	T	A	S	A	C	O
X	O	O	P	L	W	R	I	I	D	L
P	Z	B	R	E	E	E	T	R	P	U
C	C	W	I	Q	Q	Y	U	H	L	M
A	U	J	N	L	B	R	V	W	A	Y
M	H	I	T	I	E	S	P	O	Y	X
E	N	B	E	B	R	P	H	O	E	E
R	W	Q	R	Q	Q	D	H	P	R	E
A	I	I	A	Y	E	D	C	O	K	O
D	D	F	E	I	L	O	S	S	N	P
A	C	O	M	P	U	T	E	R	B	E

mobile phone

1 _____

2 _____

3 _____

4 _____

5 _____

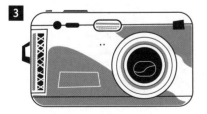

1

2

3

4

5

say it!

mobile phone

pronunciation Underline the stress in the words in exercise 1. Say the things you've got / haven't got.

I haven't got a mobile phone.

natural English *thing(s)*

2 Underline the correct word.

What's that green <u>thing</u> / things on your laptop?

1 How many thing / things are on your desk?

2 This blue thing / things is useful.

3 The digital thing / things are fantastic.

4 Does this thing / things take photos?

5 How much are the thing / things over there?

grammar *have got (= have)*

3 Complete the conversations. Use the correct form of *have*.

A Look, Ricardo <u>'s</u> got a new camera.

B Wow! It's fantastic!

A <u>¹</u> you got a DVD player?

B No, we ² _____ .

A ³ _____ your laptop got Internet access?

B Of course it ⁴ _____ .

A Where's your TV?

B We ⁵ _____ got one.

A ⁶ _____ Sandra got a mobile phone?

B Yes, she ⁷ _____ . Her number's 04474 8997653.

A ⁸ _____ they got computers in the study centre?

B I don't think so.

A I ⁹ _____ got the new Harry Potter DVD at home.

B Can I borrow it?

A Vicky and Giorgio ¹⁰ _____ got a widescreen TV.

B What make is it?

natural English giving opinions

4 Complete the conversations. Use the words in the box.

| useful | laptops | CD players | expensive | necessary | mobile phones |

A What do you think of <u>laptops</u> ?

1 B I think they're _____ .

2 A What do you think of _____ ?

3 B I don't think they're _____ .

4 A What do you think of _____ ?

5 B I think they're _____ .

write it!

Write about two things you have got and two things you haven't got. Give your opinion.

expand your vocabulary

in the office

Match the pictures with the words.

- [ ] bin /bɪn/
1. [ ] desk /desk/
2. [ ] shelf /ʃelf/
3. [ ] cupboard /ˈkʌbəd/
4. [ ] box /bɒks/
5. [ ] stool /stuːl/
6. [ ] photocopier /ˈfəʊtəʊkɒpiə/
7. [ ] noticeboard /ˈnəʊtɪsbɔːd/
8. [ ] lamp /læmp/

test yourself!

Cover the words and look at the picture above. Say the words.

expand your grammar

plural nouns

Look at the table.

singular nouns	plural nouns	rule
computer desk	computers desks	most nouns + **s**
country nationality	countries nationalities	nouns with y **y > ies**
box class	boxes classes	nouns with *s, sh, ch, x* + **es**
man / woman person child	men / women people children	irregular nouns

Cover the table. Write the singular or plural nouns.

	singular nouns	*plural nouns*
	child	*children*
1	computer	_____
2	woman	_____
3	_____	classes
4	_____	people
5	box	_____
6	_____	countries
7	desk	_____
8	nationality	_____

Tick ✓ or correct the sentences.

>   *men*
> The ~~mans~~ in the class are doctors.
> ᴧ
> My students are from Hungary. ✓

1. Javier has got two English dictionarys.

2. The new chairs are blue.

3. How many persons are in your class?

4. Three glass of white wine, please.

5. Guilia and Emilio have got four childrens.

6. The womans at the party are from Brazil.

7. Spain, Hungary, and Greece are European countries.

8. I think the new computeres are great.

wordbooster

personal things

5 Look at the picture and complete the words.

1 p e n c i l
2 m _ _ _ _ _ _ _
3 l _ _ _ _ _ _
4 k _ _
5 t _ _ _ _ _ c _ _ _

6 d _ _ _ _ _ _ _ _ _
7 n _ _ _ _ _ _ _
8 n _ _ _ _ _ _ _ _
9 b _ _ _ _ _ _ _ _

---

say it!

Say five things that you have got in your bag, briefcase, or pocket.

> I've got a lighter and a key.

possessive 's

6 Order the words to make sentences.

It / briefcase / 's / is / Susan .
It is Susan's briefcase.

1 Where / Brigitte / is / 's / calculator ?

_____

2 is / Gianni / homework / 's / difficult .

_____

3 Brad / Julia / is / boyfriend / 's .

_____

4 Simon / they / Are / coursebooks / 's ?

_____

5 Maria / bag / yellow / is / new / 's .

_____

---

think back!

How many pairs of adjectives can you remember? *terrible and great*

adjectives (1)

7 Do the crossword. Write the opposite of adjectives 1 to 6.

1 terrible   3 boring   5 safe
2 different   4 noisy   6 cheap

(crossword grid: 1 G R E A T)

say it!

pronunciation Look at the words in exercise 7. Underline the stressed syllables. Practise saying the words.

> bo<u>ring</u>

Give your opinion of these things.

cars   Madonna
e-mail   newspapers
skiing   homework

> I think newspapers are boring.

how to ... ask for things

natural English *Can I ...? / Can you ...?*

8 Match the beginnings and endings of the sentences.

	Can you turn off	_d_
1	Can I look at your	___
2	Can you help me with	___
3	Can you open the	___
4	Can I borrow	___
5	Can you turn on	___

a 20p for the coffee machine, please?

b door, please? I haven't got a key.

c exercise 2, please? It's very difficult.

d the radio, please? It's very noisy.

e the light, please? It's dark.

f magazine, please?

say it!

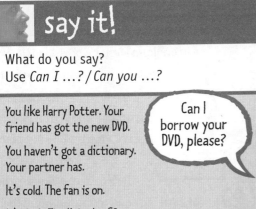

What do you say?
Use *Can I ...? / Can you ...?*

You like Harry Potter. Your friend has got the new DVD.

Can I borrow your DVD, please?

You haven't got a dictionary. Your partner has.

It's cold. The fan is on.

It's dark. The light is off.

The English homework exercises are difficult. Your sister speaks English.

grammar *this, that, these, those*

9 <u>Underline</u> the correct word.

H = headmaster, **A** = Amanda, **B** = Bill

H <u>This is</u> / That's the staffroom. Bill, ¹this is / that's Amanda, the new Spanish teacher.

B Hi Amanda, nice to meet you.

A Hi Bill!

H OK, ²this is / that's your desk and ³these / those are your shelves.

A Great. ⁴Is that / Is this my computer?

H Yes, it is. Er, ... ⁵These are / Those are the book cupboards.

A Right.

H ⁶This is / That's the coffee machine – the coffee is terrible.

A Oh, I have tea.

H Good, good. Oh, ⁷these / those are your keys.

A Thanks a lot. Er, ... where's the photocopier?

H Oh, ⁸this is / that's in the school office.

pronunciation word stress

10 Match the words with the same word stress. Then match the words with the stress pattern.

	pencil	a	important	●●
1	computer	b	Japanese	●●
2	magazine	c	syllable	●●
3	children	d	hello	●●●
4	digital	e	country	●●●
5	Brazil	f	window	●●●

three

Tick (✓) when you've done these sections.

natural English
- [ ] *a lot (of)* …
- [ ] *get to* (= arrive at a place)
- [ ] asking the time
- [ ] likes and dislikes

grammar
- [ ] present simple (1): positive, negative, and questions
- [ ] *wh-* questions
- [ ] present simple with *he / she*
- [ ] expand your grammar *and, but, because*

vocabulary
- [ ] noun groups
- [ ] leisure activities
- [ ] telling the time
- [ ] expand your vocabulary at the sports centre

you and me

grammar present simple

1 Look at the pictures of Todd and Stephy. Complete the texts with a suitable verb from the box.

work (x2)	not work	go out	not go out
play (x2)	take	live (x2)	listen to

Stephy   Jerzy

Polish girl wants friends from all over the world!

Hi! I'm 26 and I'm Polish. I *live*
in England with my boyfriend, Jerzy.
We've got a small flat in a town called
Windsor. I'm a lawyer, I <u>1   </u>
in London and in the mornings
I <u>2   </u> the train to my office.
Jerzy <u>3   </u>, he's a student.
We <u>4   </u> a lot; Windsor's got
lots of bars and restaurants and there's
also a big sports centre where we
<u>5   </u> tennis in the summer.
Hope to hear from you.
Stephy x

New friends, please!

I want to make new friends in different
countries. I <u>6   </u> in Taieri
Mouth, a small village in New Zealand.
I'm a writer and I <u>7   </u> in
my office at home. I'm 34, I'm married to
Natalia, and we've got a daughter called
Zoe. In my free time I <u>8   </u>
much. I stay in and <u>9   </u> music
or watch TV. On Saturday I <u>10   </u>
football with my friends.

I hope to hear from you soon.

Todd ☺

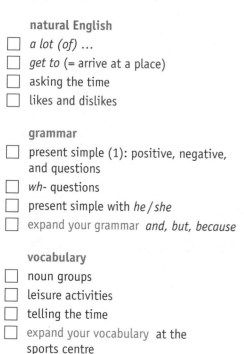

Natalia

Todd

Zoe

write it!

Write a short paragraph for the website. Include information about your home, your work / study, and your free time.

vocabulary noun groups

2 Do the puzzle.

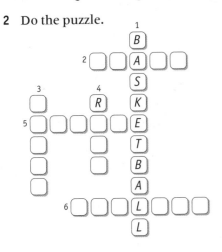

1 B
2 A
3 4 S
R K
5 E
T
B
A
6 L
L

1 a game
2 a form of transport
3 a type of home
4 a thing we eat
5 a place where we work
6 a place where we live

natural English a lot (of) …

3 Put the word in CAPITALS in the correct place.

ski
They ∧ a lot.   SKI

1 I drive lot.   A

2 They eat a lot Chinese food.   OF

3 We stay at home a.   LOT

4 They don't a lot.   GO OUT

5 You drink a lot of.   COFFEE

grammar wh- questions

4 Order the words to make questions. Then match the questions with responses a to f.

your / name / What / 's ? *What's your name?* ___b___

1 address / What / your / 's ? _____

2 you / work / Where / do ? _____

3 teach / What / you / do ? _____

4 do / When / leave / you / home ? _____

5 you / How / get / work / to / do ? _____

| a French | c 124 Elm Street | e 7.30 a.m. |
| b Karl Millstone | d by car | f at the university |

natural English get to (= arrive at a place)

5 Look at pictures 1 to 6 below. Complete the answers.

1 A How do you get to work?   B I *walk* _____.

2 A How do you get to the supermarket? B I _____.

3 A How do you get to town?   B We take _____.

4 A How do you get to school?   B We _____.

5 A How do you get to the cinema?   B We take _____.

6 A How do you get home?   B By _____.

wordbooster

leisure activities

think back!

How many leisure activities can you remember? *swimming*

6 Order the letters to make a word.

I don't like pools but I quite like (*miimswng*) s_____ in the sea.

1 Henri likes eating but he hates (*kngicoo*) c_____ .

2 Katrina doesn't like (*vnidigr*) d_____ her car in the town centre.

3 They love (*linapyg*) p_____ computer games on their new laptop.

4 Sally likes (*nppoighs*) s_____ at the new supermarket but her husband doesn't.

5 I don't like (*kiisgn*) s_____ . I think it's a dangerous sport.

6 Penny and Matt really like (*eangirtllv*) t_____ to different countries.

7 We love (*ndcniga*) d_____ . We go to a salsa club on Fridays and Sundays.

8 Do you like (*nighteessig*) s_____ when you visit new places?

telling the time

7 Draw the times on the clocks.

quarter past twelve

1 four o'clock

2 ten to six

3 twenty past nine

4 twenty-five to eleven

5 half past two

6 five to one

7 three fifteen

8 quarter to five

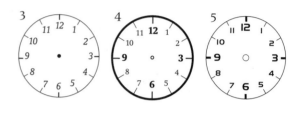

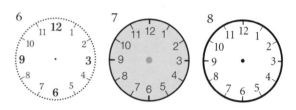

test yourself!

Cover the words in exercise 7. Say the times on the clocks.

say it!

Answer the questions.

| What time is it now? | What time do you leave the house in the morning? |
| What time is your English class? | What time do you get to work / school? |

natural English asking the time

8 Order the words to make sentences.

A what's / me / Excuse / time / the ?
Excuse me, what's the time?

1 B quarter / to / It's / four .
_____

2 A got / the / have / time / you / me / Excuse ?
_____

3 B I / Sorry / no / haven't .
_____

4 A you / Have / time / the / got / please ?
_____

5 B it's / Yes / past / three / twenty-five .
_____

how to ... talk about likes and dislikes

natural English likes and dislikes

	Rowland (R)	Anna (A)	Klaus (K)
swimming	☺☺☺	☺☺☺	☹☹☹
skiing	☺	☺☺☺	☹☹☹
computer games	☺	☹☹☹	☺
homework	☹☹☹	☹☹☹	☹
learning English	☹	☹	☺☺☺
shopping	☹☹☹	☺	☹
driving	☺☺☺	☹	☺☺☺

9 Look at the table. Complete the sentences using *really like*, *quite like*, *don't like*, and *hate*.

R I _hate_____ shopping and I ¹_____
learning English, but I ²_____ computer games
and I ³_____ swimming.

A I ⁴_____ swimming and skiing and I
⁵_____ shopping, but I ⁶_____
computer games.

K I ⁷_____ computer games but I
⁸_____ shopping. I ⁹_____
swimming and skiing, but I ¹⁰_____ driving.

say it!

Make sentences about your likes and dislikes. Use the activities in exercise 9.

grammar present simple with *he/she*

10 Complete the sentences about Angela. Use the verbs in the box in the correct form.

drive	drink	play	eat	study
live	~~work~~	listen	read	

She _works_____ at Jetair.
1 She _____ a car.
2 She _____ in an apartment.
3 She _____ to music.
4 She _____ English.
5 She _____ magazines.
6 She _____ chocolate.
7 She _____ wine and beer.
8 She _____ basketball.

11 Answer the questions about Angela.

Does she study a language?
_Yes, she does._____

1 Does she do a sport?
_____

2 Does she play computer games?
_____

3 Does she live in a house?
_____

4 Does she listen to music?
_____

5 Does she ride a motorbike?
_____

Angela

expand your vocabulary

at the sports centre

Match the words from the box with the pictures.

dance studio	~~showers~~	tennis court
swimming pool	changing room	fitness room

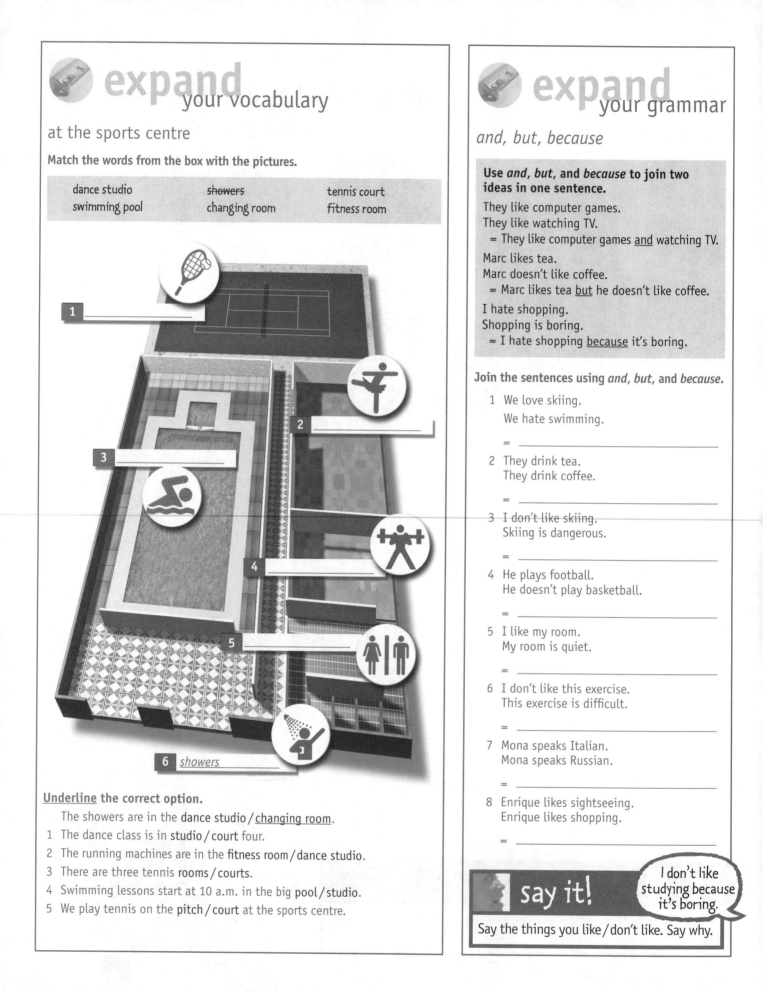

1
2
3
4
5
6 _showers_

Underline the correct option.

The showers are in the dance studio / <u>changing room</u>.

1 The dance class is in studio / court four.

2 The running machines are in the fitness room / dance studio.

3 There are three tennis rooms / courts.

4 Swimming lessons start at 10 a.m. in the big pool / studio.

5 We play tennis on the pitch / court at the sports centre.

expand your grammar

and, but, because

Use *and*, *but*, and *because* to join two ideas in one sentence.

They like computer games.
They like watching TV.
= They like computer games <u>and</u> watching TV.

Marc likes tea.
Marc doesn't like coffee.
= Marc likes tea <u>but</u> he doesn't like coffee.

I hate shopping.
Shopping is boring.
= I hate shopping <u>because</u> it's boring.

Join the sentences using *and*, *but*, and *because*.

1 We love skiing.
We hate swimming.

= _____

2 They drink tea.
They drink coffee.

= _____

3 I don't like skiing.
Skiing is dangerous.

= _____

4 He plays football.
He doesn't play basketball.

= _____

5 I like my room.
My room is quiet.

= _____

6 I don't like this exercise.
This exercise is difficult.

= _____

7 Mona speaks Italian.
Mona speaks Russian.

= _____

8 Enrique likes sightseeing.
Enrique likes shopping.

= _____

say it!

> I don't like studying because it's boring.

Say the things you like / don't like. Say why.

four

Tick (✓) when you've done these sections.

habits

vocabulary daily routines

1 Complete Maria's daily routine. Use the verbs in the box in the present simple.

| watch | get (x2) | ~~get up~~ | leave | have (x2) | read | go |

Maria is 32. She lives in a small flat in the centre of Buenos Aires and works in an office from Monday to Friday. Her days are very busy. She _gets up_____ at 7.30 a.m. She [1]_____ home at 8.30 a.m. and [2]_____ to work at 9 a.m. At 1 p.m. Maria [3]_____ lunch and she [4]_____ a magazine. Maria [5]_____ home at 7 p.m. and [6]_____ dinner. She usually [7]_____ TV until 11 p.m. and then she [8]_____ to bed.

say it!

Talk about your daily routine from Monday to Friday.

> I get up at 8 a.m.

expand your vocabulary

weekend routines

Match the pictures with the activities.

- [c] do the washing
- 1 [ ] tidy up
- 2 [ ] relax at home
- 3 [ ] clean the bathroom
- 4 [ ] go out for a drink
- 5 [ ] do the shopping

a

b

c

d

e

f

say it!

Say your weekend routine.

> I do the washing on Sunday.

---

natural English *about an hour a week*

2 Write the sentences. Use *about*.

Christina / read / day .
Christina reads about two hours a day.

1 George / sleep / night .
_____

2 Magda / work / day .
_____

3 Miguel / study English / week .
_____

4 John and Kay / watch TV / night .
_____

5 Javier / play computer games / day .
_____

expand your grammar

imperatives

Use imperatives to give instructions. Look at the examples.

Read the text.
Write an article.
Complete the sentences.

Match the pictures to the instructions. Write sentences.

| have a bath | get up | go to bed |
| make your beds | clean the bathroom | take the bus |

Get up. . 1 _____ .

2 _____ . 3 _____ .

4 _____ . 5 _____ .

grammar present simple with frequency adverbs

3 Order the words to make sentences.

a read / usually / *The Times* / I .
I usually read The Times.

b never / I / read / adventure stories .
_____

c sports magazines / sometimes / read / I .
_____

d love stories / read / usually / I .
_____

e I / on / often / read / bus / the .
_____

f hardly ever / buy / I / books .
_____

4 Put sentences a to f from exercise 3 into the conversation.

A = journalist **B** = woman in street

A Excuse me, have you got five minutes to talk about your reading habits?

B Yeah, sure.

A First of all, do you read newspapers?

B Yes, *a* _____ .

A And do you read magazines?

B Er, … ¹ _____ at the weekend.

A Where do you like to read?

B Oh, ² _____ , on my way to work.

A How many books do you buy each month?

B Oh, ³ _____ ; I usually borrow them from the library.

A What sort of books do you like?

B Well, ⁴ _____ or books about travel.

A Do you like adventure stories?

B ⁵ _____ . I don't really like them.

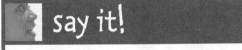

say it!

Answer the questions in exercise 4.

wordbooster

days, months, and seasons

5 Complete the text. Use the words in the box.

months	summer	March	autumn	August	~~seasons~~

New Zealand has four *seasons* _____ . They are spring, summer, ¹ _____ and winter. Each season has three ² _____ . From December to February it's ³ _____ in New Zealand. Autumn starts in ⁴ _____ and finishes in May. The winter months are June, July, and ⁵ _____ , and spring is from September to November.

time phrases with prepositions

6 Complete the conversation using *on, in, at,* or *during.*

A = Cathy, **B** = Sue

A Hi Sue. I don't usually see you *in* _____ the library.

B Oh, hi Cathy. How are you?

A Fine. Have you got time for a coffee?

B Sorry, I'm busy ¹ _____ the moment. I've got a Spanish exam ² _____ Wednesday.

A Oh bad luck! All my exams are ³ _____ July. Well, see you ⁴ _____ the weekend.

B The weekend?

A It's Tom's birthday party ⁵ _____ Saturday.

B But his birthday's ⁶ _____ the 30th, that's Thursday.

A Yeah, but he gets up early ⁷ _____ the week for work.

B What time does the party start?

A It starts ⁸ _____ 9 p.m.

B OK, see you there.

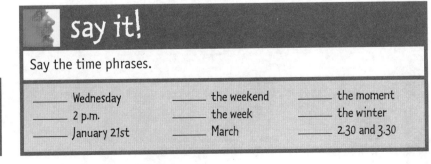

say it!

Say the time phrases.

_____ Wednesday	_____ the weekend	_____ the moment
_____ 2 p.m.	_____ the week	_____ the winter
_____ January 21st	_____ March	_____ 2.30 and 3.30

HH LEARNING CENTRE
HARROW COLLEGE

how to talk about your family

vocabulary families

think back!

How many family words can you remember? *father, cousin*

7 Read the following sentences and complete Julie's family tree.

Julie's husband is Dave. They've got two children, a girl called Rachel and a boy.

Rachel's got a brother called James.

Harry is Julie's father. He's married to Julie's mother, Anna.

Mike is Harry's brother. He isn't married.

Sylvia is James's aunt. Sylvia isn't married and she hasn't got a boyfriend.

Julie's got two brothers, John and Phil.

John hasn't got any children.

Phil's wife is called Jenny. They've got a baby daughter.

Camilla is John's girlfriend.

Rosie is James and Rachel's cousin.

natural English asking about family

8 Look at the family tree below. Match the questions and answers.

Have you got any brothers or sisters, Rachel? _e_

1 Have you got any children, Sylvia? ___
2 Have you got any cousins, Rosie? ___
3 Have you got any brothers or sisters, Phil? ___
4 Have you got any nieces or nephews, Mike? ___
5 Have you got any grandchildren, Harry? ___

a Yes, I've got two.
b No, I haven't.
c Yes, I've got three.
d Yes, I've got one brother and two sisters.
e Yes, I've got one brother.
f Yes, I've got two nephews and two nieces.

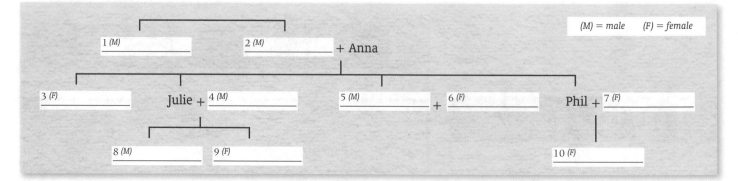

(M) = male   (F) = female

1 (M) _____ 2 (M) _____ + Anna

3 (F) _____ Julie + 4 (M) _____   5 (M) _____ + 6 (F) _____   Phil + 7 (F) _____

8 (M) _____ 9 (F) _____   10 (F) _____

grammar *my*, *your*, etc.

9 Complete the text. Use the words in the box.

> my (x2) his her (x2) its our (x2) their

Hi, I'm Krysta and I'm a teacher. I'm from Warsaw and this is the apartment block where I live with _my___ son, Jerek. ¹_____ apartment's quite small but we like it. One of the nice things about living here is that we know most of ²_____ neighbours well. My sister Jolanta has got the apartment next door. She lives with ³_____ two cats. Filip and ⁴_____ wife live at number eight. They've got two children. ⁵_____ names are Jakub and Felcia, and Jakub is ⁶_____ son's best friend. At number ten there's Kate Smith and ⁷_____ husband Simon. They're English and they've got a little dog. I think ⁸_____ name is Rex.

write it!

Write about the street or apartment block where you and your neighbours live.

natural English (*do something*) *together* /təˈgeðə/

10 Read the texts. Complete the sentences with the correct names.

Bob Masters I'm Bob. I live with my wife, Sandra. My family is quite big; I've got three children (two boys and a girl) and a granddaughter. I'm 73 and I don't work now but my days are very busy. I go shopping with my wife on Saturdays, and on Sundays I go to the swimming pool with my daughter.

Jamie Masters *I'm Jamie and I'm 33. I'm married to Patricia and we have a daughter who's three years old. I work in the town library and Patricia teaches English at Kingston School. At the weekend we play tennis and we enjoy going to the cinema. I sometimes go to the pub with my brother, John.*

Belinda Masters I'm Belinda. I'm 26. I'm a teacher at Kingston School. I'm not married but I've got a boyfriend. His name's Alan. I don't really like sport but I sometimes play golf with my brother, John. On Sundays I usually go swimming with my dad.

	_Bob_____	and	_Sandra___	go shopping together.
1	_____	and	_____	play golf together.
2	_____	and	_____	work together.
3	_____	and	_____	play tennis together.
4	_____	and	_____	go swimming together.
5	_____	and	_____	go to the cinema together.

pronunciation sounds /ð/ and /θ/

11 Say the words. Add them to the correct group.

> together   month   their   ~~Thursday~~   thanks
> birthday   ~~father~~   the   fifth   brother

/ð/	/θ/
father	Thursday

five

breakfast time

vocabulary breakfast food

1 Correct the spelling mistakes in the menu.

~ BRE̯AKFAST MENU ~

1	2 eggs on tost	£1.70	5	cerael with milk	90p
2	sasuage and egg	£1.95	6	bred, butter and jam or huney	£1.30
3	egg and bacun	£1.95	7	tea / cofee	£1.10
4	chese and harm roll	£1.45	8	fresh orange juise	£1.20

natural English *What do you have for ...?*

2 Write the answers. Use the words in (brackets).

A What do you have for breakfast?
B *I usually have tea and toast.*   (I / usually / tea / toast.)

1 A What do your children have for breakfast?
B _____ (They / always / cereal.)

2 A What does Luis have for lunch?
B _____ (He / often / sandwiches.)

3 A What do you have for lunch?
B _____ (I / never / lunch.)

4 A What do you have for dinner?
B _____ (We / sometimes / Indian food.)

5 A What does Belinda have for dinner?
B _____ (She / usually / pasta.)

say it!

What do you have for breakfast on Monday?
What do you have for breakfast at the weekend?
What do you usually have for lunch?

> I usually have tea and toast.

grammar countable and uncountable nouns

think back!

Remember which nouns are countable (C) and which are uncountable (U).

ham *(U)*   cheese   apple   egg *(C)*
sandwich   honey   sausage   tea

3 Tick ✓ a or b.

  a Can I have a sandwich? ✓
  b Can I have a piece of sandwich?

1 a Would you like some coffee?
  b Would you like an coffee?

2 a There's some water on the table.
  b There are some waters on the table.

3 a He eats a apple every day.
  b He eats two apples every day.

4 a Can I have a bread and butter?
  b Can I have a piece of bread and butter?

5 a I'd like some sausages, please.
  b I'd like a piece of sausages, please.

grammar *some / any*

4 Correct the sentences.

           any
  Have we got ~~a~~ fruit juice?

1 I'd like any cheese sandwich, please.

2 Can I have any milk with my cereal?

3 They've got a apple juice.

4 Do you want a bread?

5 Oh no! We haven't got some eggs.

wordbooster

adjectives (2)

5 Read the text. <u>Underline</u> the adjectives. Then add the adjectives to the table below.

> ## COSTA'S GREEK DINER
> ### BROOKLYN, NEW YORK.
>
> What do you think of our restaurant? Please comment below.
>
> | DATE | COMMENT | NAME |
> |------|---------|------|
> | 10/12 | It's our favourite place for eating out. The staff are very <u>friendly</u> and we like the food. | Giovanni & Gianluca (Italy) |
> | 10/12 | We like the food but the service is quite slow; it's not very cheap. | Wendy & Jim (USA) |
> | 10/12 | The people are very friendly and the food is excellent. | Marina (Argentina) |
> | 10/12 | Costa's is very clean but the tables and chairs are uncomfortable. | Marek (Poland) |

positive ☺	negative ☹
friendly	unfriendly
1	expensive
comfortable	2
3	dirty
4	awful
fast	5

test yourself!

Cover the positive adjectives and remember the negative adjectives. Cover the negative adjectives and remember the positive adjectives.

food

6 Find the words for these things in the puzzle. Write the words.

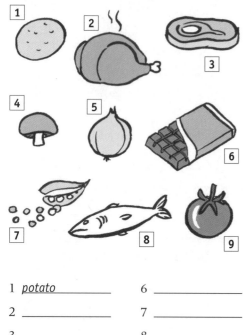

1 _potato_	6 _____
2 _____	7 _____
3 _____	8 _____
4 _____	9 _____
5 _____	

```
P O T A T O T S S H S
O P H L P Q M T P P T
C W X I M K U B E L E
H D P F F U S I A E A
I N R R O S H V S T K
C U U U N L R P X J H
K S S A I Z O A Z I U
E S C H O C O L A T E
N D Y P N O M M S V H
I K U L B N M F I S H
O T O M A T O E L C M
```

say it!

Say the things you eat and the things you don't eat. Use the words in the puzzle.

I eat potatoes but I don't eat peas.

expand your grammar

nouns that can be countable and uncountable

Some countable nouns can also be uncountable.		
C (countable) singular form	**C (countable) plural form**	**UC (uncountable)**
an ice cream	some ice creams	some ice cream

Look at the pictures. Complete the sentences with *a*, *an*, **or** *some*.

1 Dad, can I have _an_ ice cream?
2 I'd like _____ chicken, please.
3 I'd like _____ potatoes and onions.
4 I'd like _____ chicken, please.
5 Can I have _____ potato?
6 Mum, can we have _____ ice cream?

natural English *What kind of ...?*

7 <u>Underline</u> the correct answer.

    A What kind of wine / ham / <u>soup</u> have you got?
    B Er,... We've got mushroom or chicken today.

1 **A** What kind of fruit juice / coffee / water do you want?
  B Cappucino, please.

2 **A** What kind of jam / fruit / ice-cream have they got?
  B Chocolate or vanilla.

3 **A** What kind of sandwich / cereal / steak do you want?
  B Can I have cheese and tomato, please?

4 **A** What kind of tea / mineral water / wine do you drink?
  B We usually drink red.

5 **A** What kind of juice / soup / honey have you got?
  B We've only got orange.

how to ... order food

grammar *can / can't* + verb

Restaurant São Paulo

description	Brazilian restaurant in the centre of Wellington
how to find us	Keystone Street, Wellington, NZ
opening hours	7 days a week 12 p.m. to 1 a.m.
food	churrasco (barbecued pork, beef, chicken, fish, sausage, and more) with salads, vegetables, rice, potatoes, & our special breads.
drink	New Zealand wines and beers
entertainment	live music on Saturdays and Sundays 11 p.m.–1 a.m.
payment	mastercard, visa, amex
smoking	no
booking	e-mail team@churries.co.nz
	phone + 64 4 162729 fax + 64 4 162728
more information	www.saopaulo.co.nz

8 Read the text. Complete the sentences. Use *can* or *can't*.

You _can_____ eat meat at the restaurant.

1 You _____ have Brazilian food at the Restaurant São Paulo.

2 You _____ get a meal at 11 a.m.

3 You _____ drink French wine at the restaurant.

4 You _____ listen to music on Tuesdays.

5 You _____ smoke in the restaurant.

6 You _____ e-mail the restaurant.

7 You _____ eat in the restaurant on Mondays.

8 You _____ pay for your meal with a credit card.

write it!

Write about a restaurant or café that you know.

Write about the food, the place, the service, the prices, and the atmosphere.

natural English ordering food

MENU
Restaurant São Paulo

MAIN COURSES	DRINKS
—	—
steak	red / white wine
--	--
fish	beer
--	--
chicken	cola / fruit juice
--	--
rice, potatoes, or french fries	coffee
--	
salad	

9 Put the conversation in order.

a	Good afternoon, ladies.	_1_
b	OK. Anything else?	____
c	No, that's all, thanks.	____
d	We'll have steak, please.	____
e	Would you like some vegetables or salad with that?	_5_
f	What would you like to eat?	____
g	And would you like anything to drink?	____
h	Good afternoon.	____
i	We'll have french fries, please.	____
j	I'll have a glass of red wine and my daughter will have a glass of cola.	____

say it!

pronunciation Remember the pronunciation of *I'll* /aɪəl/. Practise ordering food from the menu in exercise 9.

> I'll have chicken, please.

natural English asking for more

10 Complete the sentences. Use *another /*
some more.

Can I have <u>another</u> cup of coffee?

1 Can we have _____ french fries?
2 Can I have _____ chicken, please?
3 Can I have _____ bread roll?
4 Can I have _____ peas?
5 Can we have _____ bottle of
mineral water?

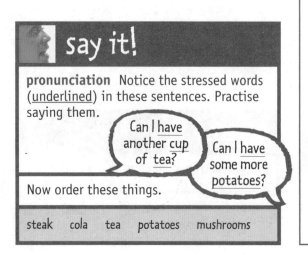

say it!

pronunciation Notice the stressed words
(<u>underlined</u>) in these sentences. Practise
saying them.

Can I have
another <u>cup</u>
of <u>tea</u>?

Can I <u>have</u>
some <u>more</u>
<u>potatoes</u>?

Now order these things.

steak   cola   tea   potatoes   mushrooms

expand your vocabulary

food groups

**Put the words into the correct food group. Use your dictionary to check
new words.**

pork chop	~~apple~~	strawberry	carrot	~~mushroom~~
bananas	turkey	sweetcorn	pepper	~~cheese~~
grapes	yoghurt	cream	~~steak~~	

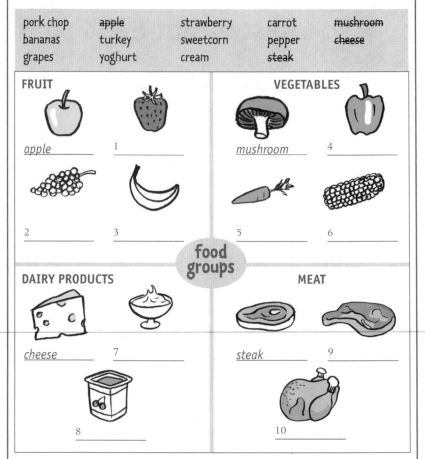

FRUIT

apple   1 _____

2 _____   3 _____

VEGETABLES

mushroom   4 _____

5 _____   6 _____

food
groups

DAIRY PRODUCTS

cheese   7 _____

8 _____

MEAT

steak   9 _____

10 _____

<u>Underline</u> the correct word.

A Would you like some <u>cream</u> / sweetcorn with your coffee?
B No, thanks. I usually drink black coffee.

1 **A** Where's the yoghurt?
   B It's in the vegetable / dairy section.

2 **A** Is there any fruit?
   B There are some grapes / peppers.

3 **A** Do you like pork?
   B No, I don't eat dairy products / meat.

4 **A** What kind of vegetables do you want?
   B Carrots / turkeys, please.

5 **A** Do you want some banana / sweetcorn ice-cream?
   B Yes, please.

how was it?

Tick (✓) when you've done these sections.

natural English
- [ ] *both*
- [ ] *How was ...?*
- [ ] saying sorry

grammar
- [ ] past simple: *was / were*
- [ ] past simple: regular and irregular verbs
- [ ] expand your grammar *before* and *after*

vocabulary
- [ ] tourist places
- [ ] past time phrases
- [ ] verb + noun collocation
- [ ] expand your vocabulary compound nouns

a day out

think back!

Think of five tourist places in your town (or a town near you).
cathedral

vocabulary tourist places

1 Order the letters to make words. The words (in brackets) are tourist places.

WALKING TOUR
Only one day in Budapest?
Try a walking tour.

We start with a visit to the Royal (*alPcea*) <u>Palace</u> .
Then we walk through the old city streets to Trinity
Square. Here, we see the beautiful 700-year-old
St Mattias ¹(*chChur*) _____ . We cross the River
Danube by the Széchenyi Chain ²(*Brdeig*) _____
and visit the National ³(*esMuum*) _____ . Then
we stop for lunch in a small Hungarian restaurant near
the Grand ⁴(*Mrktea*) _____ Hall. After lunch
we visit Vajahunyad ⁵(*ealstC*) _____ and then
we go on to City Park where you can relax and enjoy
the park.

▶ Cost 3,000 HUF (includes lunch)
▶ Meet in the hotel reception at 9 a.m.
▶ **Important: Wear comfortable walking shoes / boots.**

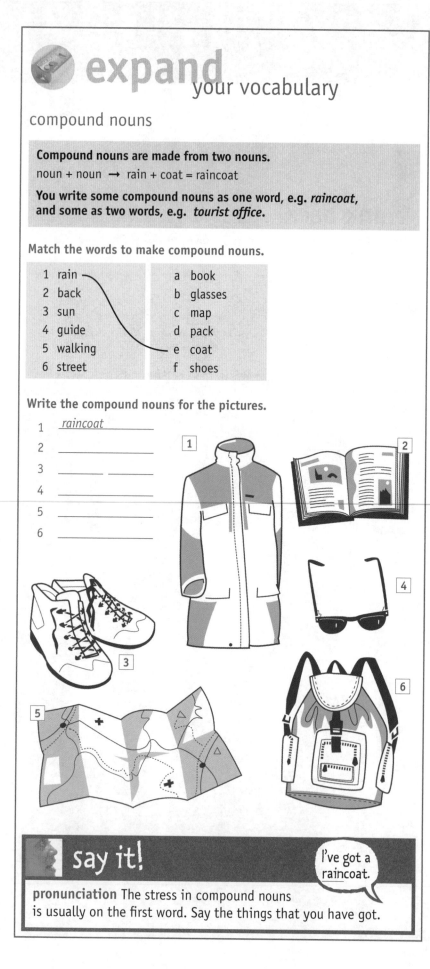

expand *your vocabulary*

compound nouns

Compound nouns are made from two nouns.

noun + noun → rain + coat = raincoat

You write some compound nouns as one word, e.g. *raincoat*, and some as two words, e.g. *tourist office*.

Match the words to make compound nouns.

1	rain	a	book
2	back	b	glasses
3	sun	c	map
4	guide	d	pack
5	walking	e	coat
6	street	f	shoes

Write the compound nouns for the pictures.

1 *raincoat*
2 _____
3 ___ _____
4 _____
5 _____
6 _____

say it!

I've got a raincoat.

pronunciation The stress in compound nouns is usually on the first word. Say the things that you have got.

grammar past simple: *was / were*

2 <u>Underline</u> the correct word.

We wasn't / <u>weren't</u> very happy with our bus tour to Windsor yesterday.

1 The tickets was / were very expensive.

2 We was / were at the tourist office at 8 a.m. but our bus was / were late.

3 The bus was / were cold and the seats was / were uncomfortable.

4 The driver wasn't / weren't very friendly.

5 The tour guide was / were very young and he was / were boring.

6 The museum and the castle was / were closed.

7 The food at the restaurant was / were awful.

8 We was / were very tired at the end of the day.

3 **Read the sentences in exercise 2. Answer the questions below.**

Were they happy with their bus tour?
No, they weren't.

1 Were the tickets cheap?

_____

2 Was their bus late?

_____

3 Was the tour guide interesting?

_____

4 Was the castle closed?

_____

5 Were they tired at the end of the day?

_____

natural English *both*

4 Test your general knowledge.
Tick (✓) the correct answer.

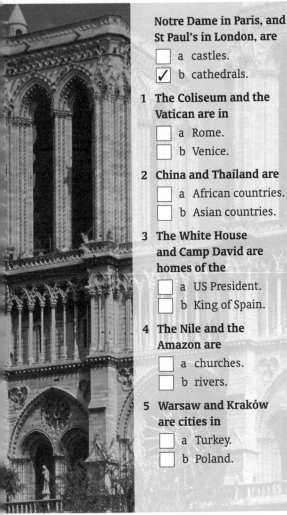

Notre Dame in Paris, and
St Paul's in London, are
- ☐ a castles.
- ✓ b cathedrals.

1 The Coliseum and the
Vatican are in
- ☐ a Rome.
- ☐ b Venice.

2 China and Thailand are
- ☐ a African countries.
- ☐ b Asian countries.

3 The White House
and Camp David are
homes of the
- ☐ a US President.
- ☐ b King of Spain.

4 The Nile and the
Amazon are
- ☐ a churches.
- ☐ b rivers.

5 Warsaw and Kraków
are cities in
- ☐ a Turkey.
- ☐ b Poland.

answer key 1a, 2b, 3a, 4b, 5b

Rewrite the information from the quiz
using *both*.

Notre Dame and St Paul's are both cathedrals.

1 _____

2 _____

3 _____

4 _____

5 _____

wordbooster

past time phrases

5 Order the words to make sentences.

to / went / 2003 / They / Miami / in .
They went to Miami in 2003.

1 yesterday / bus / Our / was / morning / late .

_____

2 night / I / was / last / tired .

_____

3 a / museum / days / We / at / few / ago / were / the .

_____

4 in / 2001 / was / Thailand / in / Roger .

_____

5 ten / my / birthday / was / ago / It / days .

_____

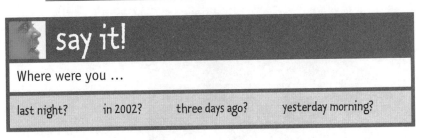

say it!

Where were you …

| last night? | in 2002? | three days ago? | yesterday morning? |

verb + noun collocation

6 Complete the sentences with a verb from the box.

| do | meet | go (x2) | stay | wash | play | go out | clean |

Do you want to *go* for a walk?

1 Ricardo hardly ever _____ his flat.

2 I often _____ my friends for a drink after work.

3 Do you want to _____ to Sam's party on Friday?

4 Selina often _____ at home and watches DVDs.

5 My mum always _____ with her friends on Friday night.

6 They usually _____ their homework after school.

7 Do you often _____ cards?

8 David usually _____ the car on Sundays.

test yourself!

Cover the answers to exercise 6.
Say the verb + noun collocations, e.g. *go – for a walk*.

how to... talk about last weekend

natural English *How was ...?*

7 Complete the sentences with a suitable adjective.

How was your weekend?

It was g r e a t . I went to Sam's party and met a really nice girl.

1   L _ _ _ _ _. We went to Paris and we had a fantastic time.

2   It was n _ _ _. I met some friends for a drink.

3   A bit b _ _ _ _ _! I went shopping with my wife.

4   It was t _ _ _ _ _ _ _. We went for a walk with the children and it rained.

5   Not very i _ _ _ _ _ _ _ _ _. I stayed at home and watched TV.

write it!

Write a diary for your weekend.

grammar past simple: regular and irregular verbs

8 Write the past form of the verbs.

have   *had*

1 watch _____		6 want _____
2 buy _____		7 clean _____
3 decide _____		8 like _____
4 meet _____		9 go _____
5 get up _____		10 stay _____

9 Complete the conversation. Use the verbs from exercise 8.

Katie Morning Jan. Sorry I'm late.

Jan Hi Katie! How was your weekend?

Katie Saturday was a bit boring. John *wanted* to go shopping and we ¹_____ to go to the shopping centre in Dublin.

Jan Yeah?

Katie We were there for about three hours and he ²_____ one thing, a raincoat. Yesterday, we ³_____ at home. I ⁴_____ the house and then we ⁵_____ the new Johnny Depp film on DVD.

Jan Is it good?

Katie Yes. We ⁶_____ it. Do you want to borrow it?

Jan Yes, please.

Katie Anyway, how was your weekend?

Jan Oh, I ⁷_____ a lovely weekend. We ⁸_____ late and on Saturday, we ⁹_____ to Wicklow for lunch at a new fish restaurant. Yesterday, we ¹⁰_____ Sunita and Phil for a drink.

Katie Oh, right. Are they well?

Jan Yeah, they're both fine. Do you want a cup of coffee?

expand your grammar

before and after

Katie and John went to the clothes shop BEFORE the music shop.
Katie and John went to the music shop AFTER the clothes shop.

Choose the correct word.

Klaus went to Paris
<u>before</u> / after he went to Rome.

1 Kemal washed his car
before / after he had lunch.

2 Jan had a coffee
before / after she got to work.

3 John and Ramsey went for
a drink before / after they played
football.

4 We went for a walk
before / after dinner.

5 Jane's birthday was
before / after John's birthday.

natural English saying sorry

10 Complete the sentences.

A I'm sorry, I _'m_____ late.

B _1_____'s fine. Are you okay ?

A Yeah, I'm fine, thanks. My train
   _2_____ late.

B Don't _3_____ . We can start now.

A Tom, Sally! You're here!

B Hello, Sandra. I'm _4_____ we're
   late. We had a problem with the car.

A _5_____ worry. Come in and have
   a drink.

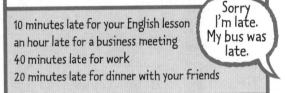

say it!

You are in the following situations. Say
you are sorry and give a reason.

10 minutes late for your English lesson
an hour late for a business meeting
40 minutes late for work
20 minutes late for dinner with your friends

> Sorry
> I'm late.
> My bus was
> late.

pronunciation /ɔː/, /ɜː/, and /ɒ/

11 Say words 1–5. <u>Underline</u> the words,
a or b, with the same sound.

Turkey /ɜː/	**a** watch	**b** <u>Germany</u>
1 coursebook /ɔː/	**a** boring	**b** doctor
2 talk /ɔː/	**a** Brazil	**b** sport
3 church /ɜː/	**a** market	**b** were
4 shopping /ɒ/	**a** worker	**b** got
5 coffee /ɒ/	**a** Australia	**b** student

say it!

> Turkey,
> Germany

Say the words with the same sound.

seven

Tick (✓) when you've done these sections.

natural English
- [ ] link words: *then / after that*
- [ ] *quite* and *very*
- [ ] *What's he / she like?*
- [ ] *When did you last …?*

grammar
- [ ] past simple: negatives
- [ ] past simple: questions
- [ ] object pronouns
- [ ] expand your grammar possessive pronouns: *mine, yours, his,* etc.

vocabulary
- [ ] life story
- [ ] appearance
- [ ] character
- [ ] expand your vocabulary synonyms

before he was famous

vocabulary life story

1 Complete the text with the verbs in the box.

was born	had	left	went
became (x2)	grew up	worked	got married

Hollywood star Arnold Schwarzenegger lives in California with his wife and children. His films are popular all over the world. In 2004 Arnie *became*_____ the Governor of California.

Arnold Alois Schwarzenegger ¹_____ in1947 and ²_____ in the small village of Thal, in Austria. He ³_____ school at 18 and he ⁴_____ to university in Munich. In Munich, Arnold lived in a small flat and ⁵_____ in a gym.

In 1966, after two years in Munich, Arnold went to America and ⁶_____ an actor. He acted in his first American film *Hercules in New York* in 1970. Then he went on to star in multi-million dollar films such as *Total Recall* and *Terminator*. He met Maria Shriver, the niece of US President JF Kennedy, at a tennis tournament. He ⁷_____ to her in 1986 and they ⁸_____ their first child, Katherine, in 1989.

write it!

Write your life story. Use the verbs in exercise 1.

grammar past simple: negatives

Antonio Banderas was born in 1960 and grew up in Málaga, a large town in the south of Spain. He moved to Madrid in 1981 and joined the National Theatre of Spain. After that, he worked as an actor in the Spanish film industry. In 1991 Antonio moved to America because he wanted to work in Hollywood. He acted in his first American film *The Mambo Kings* in 1992. His films include *Evita* with Madonna, *The Mask of Zorro*, and *Spy Kids*. In 1996 he got married to American actress Melanie Griffiths.

2 Write sentences to say how Antonio Banderas's life is different to Arnold Schwarzenegger's. Use the words in brackets.

(born / 1947)
He wasn't born in 1947.

(grow up / Austria)
He didn't grow up in Austria.

1 (go / university)

2 (work / gym)

3 (go / America / 1966)

4 (act / first American film / 1970)

5 (married / 1986)

grammar past simple: questions

3 Match the questions and answers about Arnold Schwarzenegger.

When was he born?
1 Where did he grow up?
2 Did he leave school at 18?
3 Was Arnold at university in America?
4 Why did he go to America?
5 What was the name of his first film?

a *Hercules in New York.*
b No, he wasn't.
c He wanted to be a film star.
d In a small village in Austria.
e Yes, he did.
f In 1947.

natural English link words: *then / after that*

4 Are the sentences true ✓ or false ✗?

Arnold and Maria got married, and then they had a baby. ✓

1 I learned Spanish and after that, I learned French.

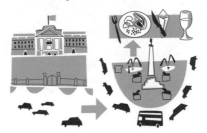

2 We saw Buckingham Palace, then we walked to Trafalgar Square. After that, we went out for lunch.

3 Julio bought a house, then he left university. After that, he worked in an office.

4 Giorgio left work and then he went for a drink with his friends. After that, he went home.

5 Ana and Sabrina got up, then they went to school. After that, they had breakfast.

wordbooster

natural English *quite* /kwaɪt/ and *very*

5 Describe the people in the picture with words from the box.

quite short	very tall	very short	~~tall~~	short	quite tall

1 _tall_

2 _____

3 _____

4 _____

5 _____

6 _____

think back!

Remember two more words to describe appearance and two more words to describe character. *good-looking, interesting*

appearance

6 Complete the descriptions.

He's tall and a bit f _a t_ .

She's got [1] m _ _ _ _ _ -length [2] d _ _ _ brown hair.

He's got [3] s _ _ _ _ hair, [4] a b _ _ _ _ and a [5] m _ _ _ _ _ _ _ _ .

He's quite [6] t _ _ _ , he's got [7] b _ _ _ _ _ hair, and he's very [8] good-l _ _ _ _ _ _ .

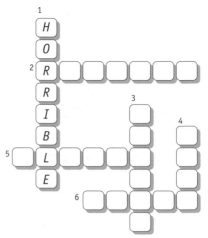

say it!

You're meeting someone at the airport. Describe your appearance.

character

7 Complete the crossword with the opposites of 1 to 6.

1 nice
2 strict
3 interesting
4 hard-working
5 stupid
6 serious

```
          1
          [H]
          [O]
    2 [R][ ][ ][ ][ ][ ]
          [R]          3
          [I]         [ ]          4
          [B]         [ ]         [ ]
    5 [ ][L][ ][ ][ ][ ]         [ ]
          [E]         [ ]         [ ]
             6 [ ][ ][ ][ ][ ]
                        [ ]
```

test yourself!

Cover the puzzle clues. Say the opposites of the words in the puzzle, e.g. The opposite of *horrible* is *nice*.

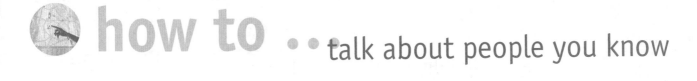

how to ... talk about people you know

grammar object pronouns

8 Complete the conversation with *me, you, it, him, her, us,* and *them*.

Peter   Hey, what's this?

Liza   That's my school photo, give *it*_____ to me!

Peter   I can't see ¹_____ in it.

Liza   That's ²_____, with the long hair and glasses. Those are my friends, Debbie and Barbara. You met ³_____ at our wedding! And that's Steven, I went out with ⁴_____ for a week when I was 14.

Peter   Who's the tall man with the beard?

Liza   That's Mr Crawley. I hated ⁵_____; his lessons were really boring. The blonde woman was our French teacher, Madame Dupont. I saw ⁶_____ last week in the supermarket.

Peter   You're all very happy here.

Liza   Yeah, the teachers told ⁷_____ to smile!

Peter   Well, what do you want to do with the photo?

Liza   Put ⁸_____ in that box.

natural English *What's he / she like?*

9 Underline the correct answer.

A   What's your husband like?
B   He's very funny / <u>hard-working</u>. He's always at the office.

1   A   What's your sister like?
    B   She's very serious / friendly. She knows lots of people.

2   A   What's your French teacher like?
    B   Boring / Interesting. I always want to sleep in his lessons!

3   A   What's your brother like?
    B   He's very stupid / clever. He passed all of his exams.

4   A   What's your sister like?
    B   She's quite lazy / strict. She never cleans the house.

5   A   What's your father like?
    B   He's horrible / nice. He always helps people.

natural English *When did you last ...?*

10 Order the words to make questions.

did / your / When / see / parents / last / you ?
When did you last see your parents?

1   did / last / french fries / you / eat / When ?
_____

2   your / washed / When / you / was / time / car / the / last ?
_____

3   did / When / last / English / you / speak ?
_____

4   play / you / did / last / When / football ?
_____

5   travelled / was / When / time / train / the / by / you / last ?
_____

say it!

What are you like? Describe your character.

say it!

The last time I .../ I last ...

Answer the questions in exercise 10.

expand your grammar

possessive pronouns

Complete the table. Use the words in the box.

theirs	his	ours	yours	hers	~~mine~~

That's my photo.	It's _mine_ .
They're your books.	1 They're _____ .
That's her car.	2 It's _____ .
They're his CDs.	3 They're _____ .
This is our house.	4 It's _____ .
It's their computer.	5 It's _____ .

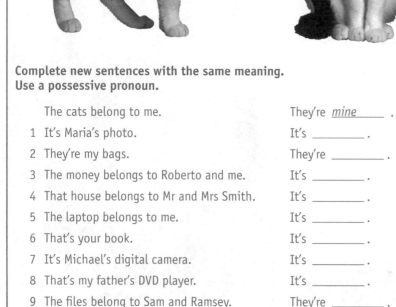

Complete new sentences with the same meaning. Use a possessive pronoun.

The cats belong to me.	They're _mine_ .
1 It's Maria's photo.	It's _____ .
2 They're my bags.	They're _____ .
3 The money belongs to Roberto and me.	It's _____ .
4 That house belongs to Mr and Mrs Smith.	It's _____ .
5 The laptop belongs to me.	It's _____ .
6 That's your book.	It's _____ .
7 It's Michael's digital camera.	It's _____ .
8 That's my father's DVD player.	It's _____ .
9 The files belong to Sam and Ramsey.	They're _____ .
10 It's my mother's mobile phone.	It's _____ .

expand your vocabulary

synonyms

Synonyms are words that have similar meanings. Look at the examples.

male / man   begin / start
road / street   small / little

Write the words in the box next to their synonyms. Use a dictionary to check new words.

~~attractive~~	nice	thin	boring
fat	relaxed	funny	clever
blonde			

pretty	_attractive_		_A_
1 slim	_____		___
2 amusing	_____		___
3 dull	_____		___
4 fair	_____		___
5 intelligent	_____		___
6 plump	_____		___
7 lovely	_____		___
8 calm	_____		___

Do words 1 to 8 above describe appearance or character? Write (A) for appearance or (C) for character.

Complete the sentences. Use synonyms.

	A	I think Juan's really clever.
	B	Yes, he's a very _intelligent_ man.
1	**A**	Paul is a very boring man.
	B	I know, he's really _____ .
2	**A**	Do you think Julia is _____ ?
	B	Oh, yes. She's very attractive.
3	**A**	Is he always relaxed?
	B	Yes, he's a very _____ person.
4	**A**	His sister's quite fat.
	B	Yes, she is a bit _____ .
5	**A**	Are the children nice?
	B	Yes, they're _____ .
6	**A**	Do you think he's _____ ?
	B	Yes, he's very funny.
7	**A**	She's very slim.
	B	Yes, she is a bit _____ .
8	**A**	Are your children fair?
	B	Yes, they've both got _____ hair.

Tick (✓) when you've done these sections.

natural English
- [ ] asking for directions

grammar
- [ ] *how much / many?*
- [ ] *there is / are*
- [ ] expand your grammar infinitives of purpose

vocabulary
- [ ] getting around
- [ ] prepositions of place
- [ ] *come* and *go*; *bring* and *take*
- [ ] directions
- [ ] expand your vocabulary train travel

I got lost!

vocabulary getting around

think back!

> Look at the pictures. Why do people get lost? How many reasons can you think of?

1 Read the text. Put the pictures in order.

1	e
2	
3	
4	
5	
6	

Last Thursday I had an interview in London for a job as a tour guide with a big travel company. I had a problem with my car so I decided to take the train. My map of London was in the car and I forgot to take it with me. Anyway, I got to the station and got on the right train. When I arrived in London I asked a man for directions. Unfortunately, he gave me the wrong directions, so I arrived half an hour late for my interview.

When I left the office I didn't ask for directions to get back to the train station and I forgot the way. It was dark and it was difficult to see the street signs but eventually, I arrived at the station. I got on the 6 o' clock train to Egham and started to read my magazine. The journey to Egham usually takes half an hour so when the train stopped at 6.30, I got off. The train left and that's when I realized I was at the wrong station.

I got home at 10 p.m. that night – oh, and I didn't get the job!

I can't remember.

a b c d e f

CITY CENTRE

ASCOT

EGHAM

expand your vocabulary

train travel

0818	0830	0839	0939	1045
0834	0857	0906	1006	1115
0856	—	—	0945	1125
	0939	1039	1145
			1123

Class STD **Ticket type** DAY RETURN **Adult** ONE **Child** NIL **RTN**
Start date 15·SEP·06 **Number** 23555 5142o5268S94
From OXFORD ✱
To BRIGHTON ✱ **Valid until** 15·SEP·06 **Price** £29·50X
Route NOT LONDON 0733
2-PART RETURN
Printed 07·33 on 15·SEP·06

1256				
1305	—	1325	1420	
1318	1330	1339	1439	1545
	1357	1406	1506	1612

Match the words and definitions.

- ☐ e This is a person who travels on a train.
1. ☐ Buy your ticket here.
2. ☐ This is a ticket from A → B.
3. ☐ Go here to get on your train.
4. ☐ This is a ticket from A → B and then from B → A.
5. ☐ This gives you information about train times.

a	single	d	ticket office
b	timetable	e	~~passenger~~
c	return	f	platform

Complete the sentences. Use words a to f.

1. **A** Good morning. I'd like a ticket to Dublin, please.
   B A _single_ or a _____?
2. **A** Which _____ does the Edinburgh train leave from?
   B Number 4, over there.
3. **A** All _____ for the 9.15 train to Paris go to platform 2.
4. **A** Where can I buy a ticket?
   B There's a _____ over there.
5. **A** Tina, what time's the next train to Brighton?
   B I don't know, I haven't got a _____.

grammar *how much / many ?*

2 Read the conversation. Write questions about Nadine's holiday using *how much* or *how many*.

Fiona Did you have a good time?

Nadine Oh, it was great. Egypt's really beautiful.

Fiona Where did you go?

Nadine Well, we started out in Alexandria and then we stayed in a hotel in Cairo for four days. After that, we took a train to Luxor and Aswan. We were on the train for 14 hours and we didn't have any food.

Fiona Was Egypt expensive?

Nadine No, I took $1,000 and I bought quite a lot of things in Cairo but I've still got $350.

Fiona What did you get?

Nadine They had some fantastic jewellery; I got some beautiful rings, three gold bracelets, and some nice earrings.

Fiona So, where's my present?

Nadine Well, I got you this book about the pyramids.

	(places / visit)	_How many places did you visit?_
1	(days / stay / Cairo)	_____
2	(hours / be / on train)	_____
3	(food / have / on train)	_____
4	(money / take)	_____
5	(jewellery / buy)	_____

say it!

Answer the questions for Nadine in the exercise above. Use *none*, *a few*, *not much*, *quite a lot*, *a lot*.

> We visited a few places.

wordbooster

prepositions of place

3 Read the sentences. Write the words for the <u>underlined</u> places (1–9 in the map).

The mosque is opposite the <u>bank</u>.

The <u>museum</u> is between the mosque and the cinema.

The <u>train station</u> is at the end of the street.

There are three cars in the <u>car park</u> behind the train station.

The <u>restaurant</u> is next to the bank.

The <u>cinema</u> is opposite the computer shop.

Two people are near the <u>statue</u>.

The statue is in front of the <u>hotel</u>.

A bird is on the <u>school</u>.

1	_bank_	6	_____
2	_____	7	_____
3	_____	8	_____
4	_____	9	_____
5	_____		

test yourself!

Cover the sentences in exercise 3 and describe the map.

come and *go*; *bring* and *take*

4 Complete the dialogues with the correct form of *come*, *go*, *bring*, and *take*.

  A I think we're lost.

  B Why didn't you _bring_ a map?

1 **A** Did you go out last night?

  B Yes, it was my wife's birthday so I _____ her to the theatre.

2 **A** What did you do yesterday?

  B We _____ to the museum in the morning and the Royal Palace in the afternoon.

3 **A** Do you often _____ here?

  B Yes, this is my favourite restaurant. The food's wonderful.

4 **A** Is Tony here?

  B No, he _____ to his Spanish class on Mondays.

5 **A** Are these Mr Smith's bags?

  B Yes. Can you _____ them up to him? He's in room 203.

6 **A** I'm really hungry.

  B I _____ some extra sandwiches today. Would you like one?

7 **A** Did you _____ a guidebook?

  B No, but we can buy one in that bookshop.

8 **A** How was your weekend?

  B Great. My brother and his children _____ to visit me.

 write it!

Write a description of the street where your house, school, or office is.

I live in Rose Street. There's a shop next to my...

how to ...get around a building

grammar *there is / are*

5 Underline the correct word.

There <u>are</u> / aren't some coursebooks on the table.

1 There isn't / aren't a computer on the desk.

2 Is there a / some map of the town in the library?

3 There are / aren't some rulers in the classroom.

4 Is there a / any dictionary in the cupboard?

5 There isn't / aren't any toilets on the second floor.

natural English asking for directions

6 Complete the sentences.

A Excuse me, <u>where's</u> the photocopier?
B It's over there.

1 A Excuse me, _____ _____ any computers?
   B Yes, they're on the second floor.

2 A Excuse me, _____ are the DVDs?
   B They're on the first floor, with the videos.

3 A Excuse me. Is there a fax machine?
   B No, I'm _____ .

4 A Excuse me. Is there a café?
   B No, _____ _____ but there's a drinks machine on the first floor.

5 A Excuse me. Where are the toilets?
   B They're _____ _____ ground floor.

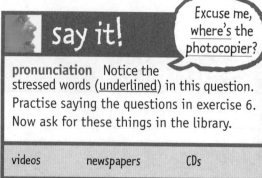

say it!

Excuse me, where's the photocopier?

pronunciation Notice the stressed words (<u>underlined</u>) in this question. Practise saying the questions in exercise 6. Now ask for these things in the library.

| videos | newspapers | CDs |

vocabulary directions

7 Follow the directions from reception. Write what the visitors did at the university, a to f.

a ~~He went to a meeting.~~	d He sent an e-mail.
b She borrowed a book from the library.	e They had an exam.
c We spoke to the Japanese teacher.	f He used the toilets.

Turn left and go along the corridor, then turn right. It's the third door on your left. *a*

1 Turn right, it's at the end of the corridor. ___

2 Turn left, go along the corridor, then turn right. They're at the end of the corridor, on your left. ___

3 Turn right, it's the first door on your left. ___

4 Turn left, it's the room at the end of the corridor. ___

5 Turn left, go along the corridor, then turn right and go to the end of the corridor. Turn right again, it's the second door on your right. ___

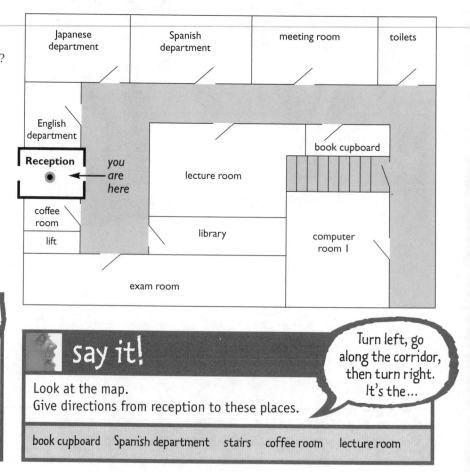

say it!

Look at the map.
Give directions from reception to these places.

Turn left, go along the corridor, then turn right. It's the...

| book cupboard | Spanish department | stairs | coffee room | lecture room |

42 unit eight

expand your grammar

infinitives of purpose

An infinitive is *to* + a verb e.g. *to go, to see, to have.*

We use infinitives of purpose to show why someone does something. Look at the examples.

Layla went to the train station **to meet her friend.**

They went to a restaurant **to have lunch.**

They went to the cinema **to see a film.**

Match the questions and answers.

Why did you go to the train station?

1 Why do they walk to work?

2 Why do you want to go to the café?

3 Why did he get a timetable?

4 Why did you go to the pub on Friday?

5 Why do you want a computer?

6 Why did he buy that map?

7 Why did you buy a dictionary?

8 Why did they buy a digital camera?

a To see where Sally's new house is.

b To save money.

c To take the train to London.

d To meet some friends.

e To check my spelling.

f To send e-mails to my friends.

g To take photos on holiday.

h To find out the times of the buses to Madrid.

i To buy a sandwich.

pronunciation /ʃ/, /tʃ/, and /dʒ/

8 Complete the texts. Use the words in the box that have the same sound as the underlined letters in each person's name.

sau<u>s</u>ages	Ru<u>ss</u>ia	<u>ch</u>ef	fi<u>sh</u>
<u>ch</u>ips	~~Jamaica~~	<u>Ch</u>ina	journalist
tea<u>ch</u>er			

<u>G</u>eoff Bri<u>dg</u>es /dʒ/

Geoff lives in

Jamaica _____ .

He's a

1 _____ .

His favourite food is

2 _____ .

Nata<u>sh</u>a Pu<u>sh</u>kina /ʃ/

Natasha lives in

3 _____ .

She's a

4 _____ .

Her favourite food is

5 _____ .

<u>Ch</u>erry <u>Ch</u>ang /tʃ/

Cherry lives in

6 _____ .

She's a

7 _____ .

Her favourite food is

8 _____ .

nine

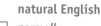 ## backpacking

grammar *have to / don't have to / do I have to ...?*

1 Read about Sunny Reef Camp Site. Are sentences 1 to 8 true ✓ or false ✗ ?

You have to make your breakfast. ✗

1 You don't have to be 18 years old to use the bar.
2 You have to share the kitchen.
3 You have to be quiet after 11 o'clock at night.
4 You have to clean the shower after you use it.
5 You have to check in before 2 o'clock in the afternoon.
6 You don't have to pay for your car.
7 You have to book online.
8 You don't have to pay when you arrive.

Sunny Reef Camp Site
(Open May–September)

FACILITIES

- ✓ Swimming pool (8.00 a.m.–8.00 p.m.)
- ✓ Café serving breakfast and lunch
- ✓ Restaurant (open from 7 p.m. for dinner)
- ✓ Bar (over 18s only)
- ✓ Kitchen (bring your own cooking equipment)
- ✓ Shop

CAMP SITE RULES

- no smoking
- no noise after 11 p.m.
- clean kitchen and shower after use
- check in after 2 p.m.
- check out before 11 a.m.

PRICES
(pay on arrival)

Tent	$9.50 per night
Adult	$6.00 per night
Children (over 5s)	$3.75 per night
Cars	$5.00 per night

Pay by *credit card, cash, or cheque.*

ADVANCE BOOKING (July and August) **by phone** 08 9782....... **online** www.sunnyreef.

pay on arrival pay when you arrive

2 Look at the camp site information (on page 44). Answer the questions.

Do I have to check in after 2 p.m.?
Yes, you do.

1 Do I have to pay for my baby?
_____

2 Do I have to bring my own cooking equipment?
_____

3 Do I have to eat in the restaurant?
_____

4 Do I have to book by telephone?
_____

5 Do I have to pay by credit card?
_____

grammar *can / can't* (permission)

3 Look at the camp site information. Complete the sentences with *can* or *can't*.

You *can*_____ swim in the mornings.

1 You _____ have breakfast in the restaurant.

2 You _____ go into the restaurant at 8 p.m.

3 You _____ buy food in the camp site.

4 You _____ smoke in the shop.

5 Children _____ eat or drink in the bar.

test yourself!

Cover the sentences in exercise 3 and look at the brochure. Say what you can and can't do at the camp site.

say it!

Say two things that you can do and two things that you can't do in your school or office.

expand your grammar

short answers

Look at the examples.

question	short answer (*long answer*)	
<u>Have</u> you got a dictionary?	Yes, I have (*got a dictionary*). No, I haven't (*got a dictionary*).	~~Yes, I've got.~~
<u>Did</u> he enjoy his holiday?	Yes, he did (*enjoy his holiday*). No, he didn't (*enjoy his holiday*).	~~Yes, he enjoyed.~~
<u>Can</u> I pay with my credit card?	Yes, you can (*pay with your credit card*). No, you can't (*pay with your credit card*).	~~Yes, you can pay.~~

Write short answers to the questions.

Is he your student?   No, he *isn't*_____ .

1 Does he like swimming?   Yes, he _____ .

2 Was the bus late?   Yes, it _____ .

3 Can I borrow this pen?   Yes, you _____ .

4 Do you live in Madrid?   Yes, I _____ .

5 Did they play football last week?   No, they _____ .

6 Has your father got a car?   Yes, he _____ .

7 Are they Italian?   Yes, they _____ .

8 Has she got any money?   Yes, she _____ .

natural English *normally* /ˈnɔːməli/

4 Match the questions and answers.

Where do you normally go on holiday?   a   at a camp site

1 Where do you normally stay?   b   by train

2 When do you normally go?   c   my backpack and a tent

3 Who do you normally go with?   d   Germany

4 How do you normally travel?   e   my boyfriend

5 What do you normally take?   f   August

say it!

Answer the questions in exercise 4.

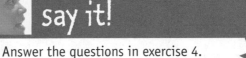

I normally go to Spain.

wordbooster

numbers (2)

5 Look at the price list for the Zeus Family Hostel in Athens. Match the figures 1 to 5 with the words a to f.

ZEUS FAMILY HOSTEL

ROOMS PER NIGHT adults €24.25 children €14.50

MEALS breakfast €4.35 lunch / dinner €13.45

EXTRAS internet access €2.90 per hour faxes €1.80

€24.25	a two euros ninety
1 €1.80	b fourteen euros fifty
2 €14.50	c four euros thirty-five
3 €2.90	d twenty-four euros twenty-five
4 €13.45	e thirteen euros forty-five
5 €4.35	f one euro eighty

6 Complete the Taylors' bill using the numbers a to f below.

ZEUS FAMILY HOSTEL
Dorou Street, Athens

Date.........24.08.05..........
Name....*Taylor Family*....
Number of nights.....2.....
Number of adults.....2.......   c   _____
Number of children...3.....   1   _____

Meals
Breakfast.........10.........   2   _____
Dinner...............5...........   3   _____

Extras
Internet....*3 hours*......   4   _____
Faxes..........2............   5   _____

TOTAL....................€307.05

a forty-three euros fifty
b three euros sixty
c ~~ninety-seven euros~~
d eight euros seventy
e sixty-seven euros twenty-five
f eighty-seven euros

think back!
Think of five more money words.
credit card

money

7 Match the beginnings and endings of the sentences.

	The shop sells	*g*
1	Did you buy a	_____
2	We had to pay a	_____
3	Antonio didn't spend	_____
4	We decided to share the	_____
5	Maria paid for the room	_____
6	How much did the holiday	_____
7	You usually have to pay	_____
8	We booked for four nights and	_____

a 10% service in restaurants.
b with her credit card.
c restaurant bill, so I paid half.
d new backpack for your holiday?
e much money in Belgium.
f saved €100.
g ~~food and newspapers.~~
h 10% deposit when we booked.
i cost?

how to ... book a room

vocabulary hotels

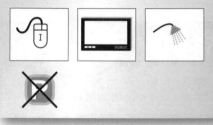

YOTEL

All for £70 a night in *central* London!

Simon Woodroffe's ideas for YOTEL came from British Airways first class and Japanese capsule hotels.

The 10.5m² double rooms have:

FORMULE 1

Just Imagine, a low price hotel in the city centre!

372 hotels in France, South Africa, Australia, the United Kingdom, Germany, Belgium, Spain, Sweden, the Netherlands, Switzerland, Brazil, and Japan.

Our double rooms are modern and all of them have colour TV.

Toilets and showers are outside the room.

Breakfast is €3.40 and is served in the breakfast bar from 6.30–9.30 a.m. weekdays and 7.30–10.30 a.m. on Saturdays and Sundays.

HOTEL HK

One of the best hotels in the world.

We have 531 double and twin bed en-suite rooms in the centre of Hong Kong with:

Other facilities include:
- swimming pool
- 8 restaurants and bars
- gym
- parking

The price of your room includes all meals.

---

8 Read the descriptions of the three hotels and complete the table.

	Yotel	Formule 1	Hotel HK
double rooms	✓	✓	✓
1 en-suite rooms			
2 bath			
3 shower			
4 Internet access			
5 parking			
6 swimming pool			
7 gym			
8 restaurant			
9 bar			
10 breakfast included in price			

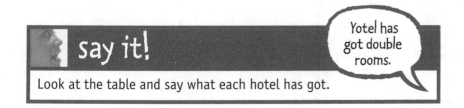

say it!

Look at the table and say what each hotel has got.

> Yotel has got double rooms.

---

natural English *I (don't) think so*

9 Order the words to make questions.

en-suite / Has / got / it / rooms ?

A *Has it got en-suite rooms?*

B I don't think so.

1 got / pool / hotel / Has / a / the ?

A _____

B I don't think so.

2 it / a / restaurant / Has / got ?

A _____

B I don't think so.

3 gym / there / Is / a ?

A _____

B I don't think so.

4 breakfast / the / included / Is / price / in ?

A _____

B I don't think so.

5 Are / any / available / there / rooms ?

A _____

B Yes, I think so.

expand your vocabulary

hotel rooms

Picture of a hotel room with labels a–i

Match the words with the pictures.

- **b** towel /ˈtaʊəl/
- 1 ☐ sheet /ʃiːt/
- 2 ☐ blanket /ˈblæŋkɪt/
- 3 ☐ hanger /ˈhæŋə/
- 4 ☐ kettle /ˈketl/
- 5 ☐ balcony /ˈbælkəni/
- 6 ☐ pillow /ˈpɪləʊ/
- 7 ☐ fan /fæn/
- 8 ☐ mirror /ˈmɪrə/

Underline the correct word.

A Can I have another towel / <u>blanket</u> for my bed?
B Yes, of course.

1 **A** Could I have some sheets / hangers for my clothes?
B Certainly. Here you are.

2 **A** It's quite hot in here.
B Turn on the fan / mirror.

3 **A** Could we have some more pillows / balconies?
B Of course.

4 **A** There's a kettle / hanger and some tea and coffee in every room.
B That's good, we can make a drink.

5 **A** Has the room got a sheet / balcony?
B No, I'm afraid not.

write it!

Complete the e-mail to the Hotel HK to book a room. Include the following information.

number of nights	dates	en-suite bath / shower
smoking / non-smoking	double / single / twin room	balcony

Dear Sir/Madam,
I would like to book a room at the Hotel HK for ... nights.

natural English *Would you prefer ...?*
/ˈwʊdjə prɪˈfɜː/

10 Who says these things? Write R for receptionist and W for waiter.

Would you prefer a table in a
smoking or non-smoking area? *W*

1 Would you prefer the first floor
or the second floor? ___

2 Would you prefer meat or fish? ___

3 Would you prefer potatoes or chips? ___

4 Would you prefer a double or twin? ___

5 Would you prefer a bath or a shower? ___

6 Would you prefer to sit near the
window? ___

7 Would you prefer breakfast in your
room? ___

8 Would you prefer a balcony? ___

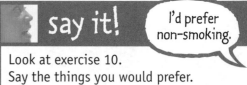

say it!

I'd prefer non-smoking.

Look at exercise 10.
Say the things you would prefer.

natural English
suggesting and responding

11 Match the suggestions and responses.

Let's have a party tonight. *e*

1 We could go to the cinema. ___

2 We could go to a French
restaurant. ___

3 Let's go home. ___

4 We could stay at the
Plaza Hotel. ___

5 Let's have a drink. ___

a That's a good idea. I'm quite thirsty.

b I'm not sure about that. The rooms
are very expensive.

c Yeah, that's a good idea. Is there
a good film on?

d Hmm, I'm not sure about that.
I'd like a pizza.

e Hmm, I'm not sure about that.
I've got an exam tomorrow.

f That's a good idea. I'm really tired.

Tick (✓) when you've done these sections.

natural English

☐ talking about ages
☐ *quite / very well*
☐ giving opinions
☐ offering help

grammar

☐ *can / can't* (ability)
☐ *something / anything / nothing*, etc.
☐ expand your grammar *somewhere / anywhere / nowhere*

vocabulary

☐ action verbs
☐ parts of the body
☐ common phrases
☐ expand your vocabulary *aches*

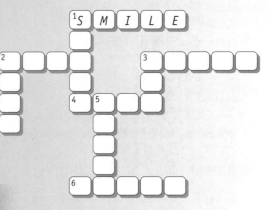

babies

think back!

Remember what babies can do at six months old. What can't they do?

vocabulary action verbs

1 Do the puzzle.

▶ **across**

1 _____ , I want to take your photo.
2 _____ goodbye.
3 How babies move.
4 The opposite of work.
6 _____ the ball to me.

▼ **down**

1 When you are tired, you want to _____ .
2 How children and adults move.
3 You do this when you are unhappy.
5 You do this when you are happy.

¹S M I L E

natural English talking about ages

2 Do the quiz.

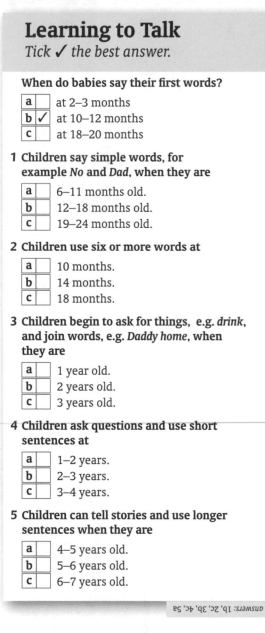

Learning to Talk
Tick ✓ the best answer.

When do babies say their first words?
- **a** ☐ at 2–3 months
- **b** ✓ at 10–12 months
- **c** ☐ at 18–20 months

1 Children say simple words, for example *No* and *Dad*, when they are
- **a** ☐ 6–11 months old.
- **b** ☐ 12–18 months old.
- **c** ☐ 19–24 months old.

2 Children use six or more words at
- **a** ☐ 10 months.
- **b** ☐ 14 months.
- **c** ☐ 18 months.

3 Children begin to ask for things, e.g. *drink*, and join words, e.g. *Daddy home*, when they are
- **a** ☐ 1 year old.
- **b** ☐ 2 years old.
- **c** ☐ 3 years old.

4 Children ask questions and use short sentences at
- **a** ☐ 1–2 years.
- **b** ☐ 2–3 years.
- **c** ☐ 3–4 years.

5 Children can tell stories and use longer sentences when they are
- **a** ☐ 4–5 years old.
- **b** ☐ 5–6 years old.
- **c** ☐ 6–7 years old.

answers: 1b, 2c, 3b, 4c, 5a

grammar *can / can't* (ability)

3 Complete the sentences with *can* or *can't*.

Babies <u>can't</u> can't say their first words at 2–3 months.

1 Children ——— say simple words at 6–11 months.

2 Children ——— use six or more words when they are ten months old.

3 Children ——— join words at 24 months.

4 Children ——— make short sentences when they are 2–3 years old.

5 Children ——— tell stories at 4–5 years.

natural English *quite / very well*

4 Circle the correct sentence, a or b.

a Marc can cook quite well.
ⓑ Marc can't cook very well.

1 a Juan can play the guitar very well.
  b Juan can't play the guitar very well.

2 a Eva can read quite well.
  b Eva can read very well.

3 a They can't understand Japanese.
  b They can understand Japanese very well.

4 a They can't dance very well.
  b They can dance quite well.

5 a Yuri can drive very well.
  b Yuri can't drive very well.

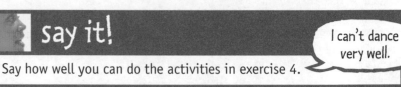

say it!

Say how well you can do the activities in exercise 4.

> I can't dance very well.

parts of the body

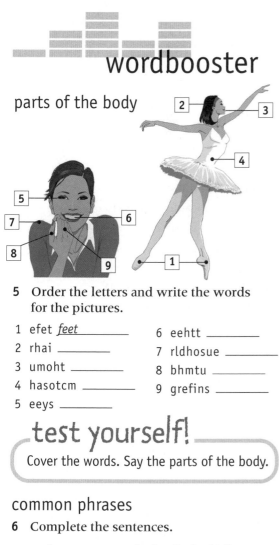

5 Order the letters and write the words for the pictures.

1 efet _feet_
2 rhai _____
3 umoht _____
4 hasotcm _____
5 eeys _____
6 eehtt _____
7 rldhosue _____
8 bhmtu _____
9 grefins _____

test yourself!

Cover the words. Say the parts of the body.

common phrases

6 Complete the sentences.

I _a_ my arm playing basketball.
a broke   b happened   c need

1 What's the ___ ?
a wrong   b matter   c happened

2 There's something ___ with the photocopier.
a happened   b terrible   c wrong

3 Can I give you a ___ to work?
a lift   b hand   c drive

4 She doesn't look very ___ today.
a fine   b terrible   c well

5 Do you ___ any help?
a look   b need   c like

write it!

Your friend wants you to go to his/her birthday party. You're not well and can't go to the party. Write an e-mail to explain.

expand your vocabulary

aches

Write the words for the pictures.

stomachache /'stʌməkeɪk/	backache /'bækeɪk/	headache /'hedeɪk/
earache /'ɪəreɪk/	neckache /'nekeɪk/	toothache /'tuːθeɪk/

neckache   1 _____   2 _____

3 _____   4 _____   5 _____

Underline the correct word.

He ate two boxes of chocolates and now he's got earache / <u>stomachache</u>.

1 She can't eat anything, she's got toothache / neckache.
2 Can you turn the TV down? I've got a headache / backache.
3 He's got toothache / backache so he can't walk very well.
4 I've got stomachache / neckache and I can't move my head.
5 The music was so loud that I had toothache / earache after the concert.

say it!

You are ill and you can't go to work.
Look at the pictures. Say what's wrong with you.

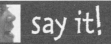

I've got neckache.

how to ...offer help

natural English giving opinions

7 Complete the sentences using *it's better to ...* and the words in brackets.

A I don't know what the problem is.

B I think *it's better to go to the garage* . (go / garage)

1 **A** Have you got any cigarettes?

B I think _____ . (stop / smoking)

2 **A** I don't understand this exercise.

B I think _____ . (ask / teacher)

3 **A** It's an hour by train, or three hours by bus.

B I think _____ . (take / train)

4 **A** It's this way.

B I think _____ . (look at / map)

5 **A** Don't worry, I can fix this.

B I think _____ . (buy / new TV)

grammar *something / anything / nothing*, etc.

8 Underline the correct word.

There wasn't someone / <u>anyone</u> sitting opposite me.

1 I didn't see someone / anyone in the street.

2 It was really cold but no-one / nothing stopped to offer me a lift.

3 There's nothing / anything I can do to help.

4 Did anyone / anything offer to help you?

5 Is no-one / anyone with you?

6 There's something / anything wrong with this CD.

7 Anyone / Someone at the supermarket offered to carry my bags.

8 Is there anything / anyone I can do to help?

9 Tick ✓ or correct the sentences.

The bag was empty. There was ^nothing something in it.

There wasn't anything in the room. ✓

1 There's something wrong with my mobile phone.

2 ~~He said anything to me but I didn't understand.~~

3 I'm really hungry. Is there nothing to eat?

4 There's something to worry about. The test is easy.

5 Did you do nothing interesting at school?

natural English offering help

10 Match the problems with the offers of help.

	I can't do this exercise.	a	Shall I call the doctor?
1	I'm late for work.	b	I'll lend you some.
2	These bags are heavy.	c	Shall I give you a lift?
3	I can't find my keys.	d	I'll help you look for them.
4	I haven't got any money.	e	I'll help you carry them.
5	I don't feel very well.	f	Shall I help you with it?

 **say it!**

Respond to the offers of help in exercise 10. Use:

Oh, thanks very much.   Yeah, thanks.   No, it's OK, thanks.

expand your grammar

somewhere / anywhere / nowhere

Look at the table.

	POSITIVE +	NEGATIVE –	QUESTION ?
people	someone	no-one	anyone
things	something	nothing	anything
places	somewhere	nowhere	anywhere

Look at the examples.

There was *nowhere* to sit on the train so we had to stand.

They went to live *somewhere* in Spain.

Complete the sentences with *somewhere, nowhere*, or *anywhere*.

Did you go *anywhere* yesterday?

1 Is there _____ interesting to visit near here?
2 They stayed at a camp site _____ in Turkey.
3 I'm bored, there's _____ to go.
4 Did Jamal and Tony go _____ at the weekend?
5 He went _____ with his brother.
6 There was _____ to go, so we stayed at home.
7 Jemma bought a beautiful bag _____ in town.
8 We stayed in a hotel _____ in the town centre.
9 The children were bored because there was _____ to play.
10 They met at a youth hostel _____ in Paris.

pronunciation sounds and spelling
(*oo* and *ou*)

11 Underline the correct spelling.

It takes a coople / <u>couple</u> of
hoors / <u>hours</u> by plane.

1 This is my new hoose / house.
2 Coold / Could I have a spoon / spoun, please?
3 I've got toothache / touthache.
4 What's the matter with your foot / fout?
5 Woold / Would you like a cup of coffee?
6 How many coontries / countries did you visit?
7 It's aboot / about 50 miles.
8 This is my coosin / cousin, Elena.

Put the underlined words in the correct row.

mouth /aʊ/	*hours,*
group /uː/	
double /ʌ/	*couple,*
took /ʊ/	

eleven

Tick (✓) when you've done these sections.

natural English
- [ ] *How long does it take?*
- [ ] agreeing and disagreeing
- [ ] *get* (= *buy*)
- [ ] recommending: *should* + verb

grammar
- [ ] comparative adjectives
- [ ] superlative adjectives
- [ ] expand your grammar *too* + adjective

vocabulary
- [ ] shops and products
- [ ] adjectives (3)
- [ ] expand your vocabulary travel nouns

from A to B

grammar comparative adjectives

1 Read the texts.

> For Valentine's Day I took my wife, Sandra, to Venice on the Orient Express train. We left London on Sunday morning, travelled through France, Switzerland, and Austria, and arrived in Venice on Monday evening. The journey was great and the train was very comfortable. There were three restaurants on the train and the meals were excellent. It was expensive; I paid over £1,000 for each ticket, but it was fantastic. (Sam, London)

> I visited my friend Rosanna in Venice last week. I got a plane ticket on the Internet for £25. The journey usually takes a couple of hours but we were delayed for four hours. The plane was awful. The seats were small, there was nothing to eat or drink, and there was no film to watch. There were lots of very noisy children on the plane too. I was very happy to get off the plane in Italy. Then I found out that my bag wasn't on the plane and I had no clean clothes. (Michael, Bournemouth)

Compare Michael and Sam's journeys. Use the adjectives in the box.

more expensive	~~faster~~	easier	~~slower~~
quieter	better	more boring	more difficult
cheaper	more interesting	noisier	worse

Sam's journey was …	Michael's journey was …
slower	*faster*
1 _____	6 _____
2 _____	7 _____
3 _____	8 _____
4 _____	9 _____
5 _____	10 _____

natural English *How long does it take?*

2 Put sentences a to f into the conversation.

a How long does it take to get to the town centre

b It took ten minutes in the taxi

c Well, the flight only takes a couple of hours

d Not long by car

e ~~How long did it take you to get here~~

f It took four hours to fix the problem

R = Rosanna; **M** = Michael

R Michael! You're here!

M Hi Rosanna. It's great to see you. How are you?

R I'm fine, but you look tired. __e__ ?

M __1__ but we were delayed in London.

R Why?

M Oh, I'm not sure. I think there was something wrong with the plane. __2__ .

R How was the journey from the airport?

M It was OK. __3__ . The driver was really fast!

R Er,… Did you bring any bags with you?

M My bag's in London; they didn't put it on the plane. I haven't got any clean clothes.

R Well, there are lots of shops in the town centre. You can buy something there.

M __4__ ?

R __5__ . I'll drive you, but let's have a coffee first.

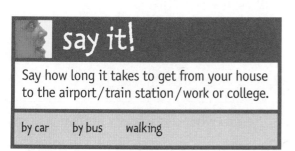

say it!

Say how long it takes to get from your house to the airport / train station / work or college.

| by car | by bus | walking |

3 Complete the sentences. Write the comparative forms of the adjectives in (brackets).

Small cars are (easy) *easier* to park than buses.

1 Rollerblading is (dangerous) ——————— than walking.

2 Riding a motorbike in winter is (cold) ——————— than travelling on a plane.

3 My car is (old) ——————— than yours.

4 Walking is (healthy) ——————— than driving.

5 In Amsterdam, bicycles are (common) ——————— than buses.

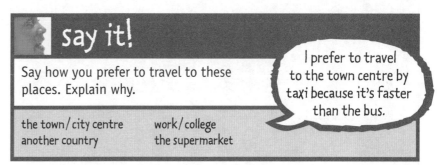

say it!

Say how you prefer to travel to these places. Explain why.

| the town / city centre | work / college |
| another country | the supermarket |

I prefer to travel to the town centre by taxi because it's faster than the bus.

natural English agreeing and disagreeing

4 Correct the mistakes.

Yes, that true.
___that's___

I think trains are better than cars.

I'm agree.
1 _____

I'm no sure.
2 _____

It depend.
3 _____

I not so sure.
4 _____

I don't agreed.
5 _____

expand your vocabulary

travel nouns

Match the words and pictures.

business trip flight tour drive cruise excursion

business trip

1 _____

2 _____

3 _____

4 _____

5 _____

Underline the correct word or phrase.

Do you often have to go on <u>business trips</u>/cruises for your company?

1 They went on a six-week **tour**/**excursion** of South America.

2 It was a nice day so we went for a **drive**/**cruise**.

3 The **flight**/**drive** from London to Sydney took 23 hours.

4 We went for a **drive**/**tour** in Henk's new car.

5 The **excursion**/**business trip** to Pompeii costs 200 euros.

6 Every year I go on a **cruise**/**excursion** around the Mediterranean Sea.

say it!

I like excursions.

Say what travel you like/don't like. Use words from the exercise.

wordbooster

shops and products

5 Look at the pictures (opposite). Find eight more products in the puzzle. Match them with the shops below.

C	H	A	I	R	S	S	D	B	W	S
S	A	A	F	X	U	B	Z	M	T	
P	H	X	E	L	G	E	E	C	A	
E	W	I	V	C	A	K	E	S	M	
R	R	X	R	Y	R	B	L	J	P	
L	B	F	O	T	Y	K	B	U	S	
A	D	M	A	V	S	T	I	I	B	
M	H	A	S	P	I	R	I	N	B	
B	P	E	M	R	E	U	I	U	V	
P	C	A	S	S	E	T	T	E	S	

supermarket   *sugar* _____

1 chemist _____

2 department store _____

3 butcher's _____

4 furniture shop _____

5 record shop _____

6 post office _____

7 clothes shop _____

8 baker's _____

natural English *get (= buy)*

6 Order the words to make sentences.

When / new / car / get / Rudy / did / his ?
When did Rudy get his new car?

1 did / What / you / at / baker's / get / the ?
_____

2 got / Milan / this / shirt / I / in .
_____

3 I / envelopes / get / Where / some / can ?
_____

4 We / get / to / some / have / chairs .
_____

5 did / Where / get / bag / you / that ?
_____

how to ... recommend

natural English recommending: *should + verb*

8 Match 1 to 5 and a to f.

> You should try that new Mexican restaurant.

1 Don't stay in that hotel.
2 You should hire a car.
3 Don't take the bus.
4 You should go to Australia.
5 You should go to the market.

a It's a great country and you can practise your English there.
b You can buy cheap fruit and vegetables there.
c The food's great.
d The train is cheaper and faster.
e It's a good way to see the country.
f It's really dirty. There's a better one near the town centre.

grammar superlative adjectives

9 Write the superlative forms of the adjectives in (brackets).

Sydney TRAVEL GUIDE

WHY? Sydney is Australia's (big) _biggest_
and 1 (friendly) _____ city, and there are
hundreds of things for tourists to do and see.

WHEN? Sydney is a great place to visit at any time
of the year but perhaps the 2 (comfortable) _____
time to come is autumn, especially March and April.

WHAT? Bondi Beach is Sydney's 3 (long) _____
and 4 (beautiful) _____ beach.
Sydney Opera House is the city's 5 (famous) _____
building, where you can sit and listen to a free music concert.

HOW? Driving and parking in central Sydney are difficult.
The 6 (cheap) _____ way to get around the city is
by bus. However, the 7 (nice) _____ way to travel
is by ferry. It's also the 8 (good) _____ way to
see the city.

adjectives (3)

7 Choose the correct word to complete the sentences.

> 'John' is a very _c_ English name.
> a healthy   b rich   c common

1 Playing sports keeps you ___ .
  a poor   b healthy   c lucky

2 We had a ___ meal in that new restaurant in town.
  a wonderful   b common   c lucky

3 Football is the most ___ sport in Slovakia.
  a rich   b popular   c busy

4 The town centre was quite ___ on Saturday.
  a wonderful   b modern   c busy

5 In China eight and nine are ___ numbers.
  a lucky   b rich   c common

6 He's very _____ ; he's got no money.
  a modern   b common   c poor

7 I'd prefer to live in a ___ flat in the city centre.
  a healthy   b modern   c busy

8 You have to be ___ to buy a house in Monaco.
  a rich   b common   c popular

write it!

Write a travel guide for your city or area. Answer the questions in exercise 9: Why? When? What? How?

10 Write sentences using the superlatives in (brackets). Use *is* or *has*.

Moscow

REYKJAVIK (Iceland)

first houses built:
874

area:
275 km²

number of people:
171,500

winter temperature
−2°C to 3°C

summer temperature
9° to 14°C

MOSCOW (Russia)

first houses built:
1147

area:
1,035km²

number of people:
8.3 million

winter temperature
−16°C to −9°C

summer temperature
13° to 23°C

SYDNEY (Australia)

first houses built:
1788

area:
2,103 km²

number of people:
4 million

winter temperature
8° to 16°C

summer temperature
18° to 26°C

<u>Reykjavik is the oldest city.</u> (oldest)

1 _____ (hottest summers)

2 _____ (biggest)

3 _____ (newest)

4 _____ (coldest winters)

5 _____ (most people)

6 _____ (smallest)

7 _____ (coldest summers)

8 _____ (fewest people)

say it!

Compare your nearest town with Moscow, Reykjavik, and Sydney.

> Madrid's hotter than Moscow and Reykjavik.

---

expand *your grammar*

too + adjective

Look at the examples.
I can't buy a coat. They're **too** expensive.
I can't work. It's **too** hot.
I want to go back to Australia. It's **too** cold here.

Make sentences using *too* + the adjectives in the box.

late	noisy	difficult	tired	small
modern	~~expensive~~	hot	big	

A Can we stay at this hotel?
B No, it's <u>*too expensive*</u>. We don't have much money.

1 **A** Do you like this town?
 B No, it's _____ . I prefer old towns.

2 **A** Is this room OK?
 B No, it's _____ . Have you got a bigger one?

3 **A** Are you going to learn Chinese?
 B No, it's _____ . English is easier.

4 **A** I want to go to Africa.
 B Africa's _____ for me. I want to go somewhere cold.

5 **A** Do you prefer to live in a city or a village?
 B Cities are _____ . I prefer to live somewhere quiet.

6 **A** Which train goes to Oxford?
 B I'm sorry, you're _____ . The Oxford train left five minutes ago.

7 **A** Why do you want to take the train to work today?
 B Because I'm _____ to drive my car.

8 **A** Why do you need a smaller travel bag?
 B This one is _____ to take on the plane.

Tick (✓) when you've done these sections.

natural English
- [ ] *How about you?*
- [ ] phoning a friend
- [ ] telephone introductions
- [ ] showing you (don't) understand

grammar
- [ ] present continuous
- [ ] present simple vs continuous
- [ ] expand your grammar verbs not usually used in the continuous

vocabulary
- [ ] clothes
- [ ] telephoning
- [ ] expand your vocabulary mobile phones

who are they?

natural English *How about you?*

1 Match the questions and answers.

Have you got any friends here?

1 Who do you go on holiday with?

2 Do you speak any other languages?

3 When did you meet your girlfriend?

4 Do you often go out with the people you work with?

5 Where do you buy your clothes?

a Yeah, French and Arabic. How about you?

b One or two. How about you?

c At the shopping centre in town. How about you?

d Yeah, once or twice a week. How about you?

e A couple of years ago. How about you?

f My brother. How about you?

say it!

Answer the questions in exercise 1.

I've got three friends here.

grammar present continuous

2 Write the names of the people in the picture.

Naila and Karen are sitting on the sofa talking.

Karen and Carlos are smoking.

Kevin and John are smiling.

Rebecca is standing near a window and listening to a man.

Rebecca and Naila are drinking wine.

Chang is talking to a young woman.

Maria and Gemma are dancing in the middle of the room.

Kevin and Chang are holding plates of food.

Maria and Naila are wearing trousers.

John and Kevin are talking.

John is wearing glasses.

1 _Karen_   6 _____

2 _____   7 _____

3 _____   8 _____

4 _____   9 _____

5 _____

3 Rewrite the sentences correctly.

They going to school.
They are going to school.

1 I is talking to my friends.

_____

2 Is Tomás and Luis working today?

_____

3 They aren't smokking.

_____

4 She listening to her CDs.

_____

5 What she wearing?

_____

6 We isn't playing computer games.

_____

7 What is those students studying?

_____

8 John and Kevin talking.

_____

test yourself!

Cover the sentences and describe the picture.

say it!

I'm doing my homework, …

Say three things that you are doing now.

wordbooster

clothes

think back!

Remember five more words for clothes.
jumper

4 Order the letters for the clothes. Do the puzzle and find a new word.

1 tobos   <u>boots</u>
2 srdes   _____
3 tha   _____
4 tskri   _____
5 njesa   _____
6 catkej   _____
7 rsith   _____
8 urtoesrs   _____
9 (new word) _____

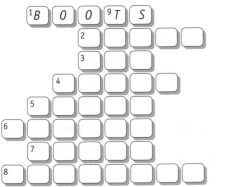

¹B O O ⁹T S
2 ☐☐☐☐☐
3 ☐☐☐
4 ☐☐☐☐☐
5 ☐☐☐☐☐
6 ☐☐☐☐
7 ☐☐☐☐
8 ☐☐☐☐☐☐☐

say it!

I'm wearing a blue skirt.

Say what you are wearing today.

telephoning

5 Choose the correct word.

Did anyone <u>b</u> when I was out?
a engage   b call   c message

1 Terry Brown _____ a message for you.
   a rang   b left   c phoned

2 I phoned but she wasn't there. I got her _____ .
   a answerphone   b no answer   c number

3 Rita's busy at the moment. Can you _____ later?
   a engage   b ring back   c leave a message

4 I called you three times last night but your phone was _____ .
   a engaged   b no answer   c answerphone

5 I need to ring Chao today but I haven't got his _____ .
   a answerphone   b message   c number

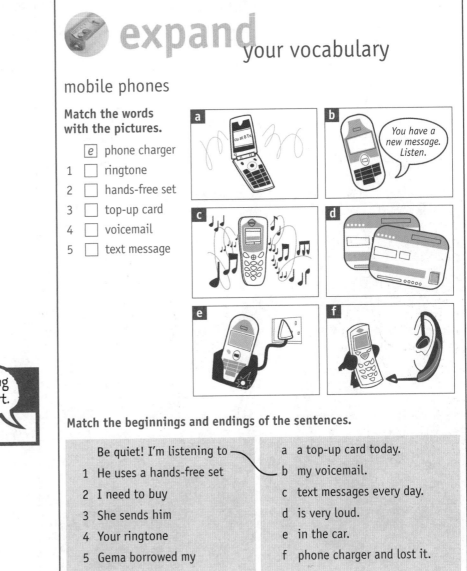

expand your vocabulary

mobile phones

Match the words with the pictures.

- [e] phone charger
1 ☐ ringtone
2 ☐ hands-free set
3 ☐ top-up card
4 ☐ voicemail
5 ☐ text message

a *cu at 8 Tx*

b *You have a new message. Listen.*

c

d

e

f

Match the beginnings and endings of the sentences.

Be quiet! I'm listening to ——   a a top-up card today.
1 He uses a hands-free set   b my voicemail.
2 I need to buy   c text messages every day.
3 She sends him   d is very loud.
4 Your ringtone   e in the car.
5 Gema borrowed my   f phone charger and lost it.

how to... use the phone

grammar present simple vs continuous

6 Underline the correct form of the verb.

Sanjiv	Emilio, what do you do / <u>are you doing</u>?
Emilio	I ¹text / 'm texting Joe to ask him to play football tonight.
Sanjiv	But today's Wednesday and we always ²play / are playing football on Wednesdays!
Emilio	Yeah, but I got a new phone yesterday and I ³practise / 'm practising.
Sanjiv	Wow, that's great! ⁴Does it take / Is it taking photos?

Jemma	Kevin, the phone ⁵rings / 's ringing.
Kevin	Well, I can't answer it, I ⁶have / 'm having a bath.

Irina	Do you want to come over to my house? I've got the new Brad Pitt DVD.
Linda	Great idea – are your parents in?
Irina	Oh no, they're out. They ⁷go / are going to the gym every Tuesday and then they usually ⁸meet / are meeting some friends for a drink.
Linda	Okay, I'll phone my mum and tell her. She ⁹works / 's working in London today.
Irina	Really? What ¹⁰does your mum do / 's your mum doing?
Linda	Oh, she's an engineer with a big oil company.

expand your grammar

verbs not usually used in the continuous

Look at the examples.

understand	Majed understands English.
	Majed's ~~understanding~~ English.
like	They like football.
	They're ~~liking~~ football.
need	Why do you need a new car?
	Why ~~are you needing~~ a new car?
want	Do you want to go out?
	~~Are you wanting~~ to go out?
know	He doesn't know my brother.
	He ~~isn't knowing~~ my brother.

<u>Underline</u> the correct words.

When <u>do you need</u> / are you needing the money?

1 Are you liking / Do you like playing tennis?
2 He wants / is wanting a glass of water.
3 Does she need / Is she needing any help with her homework?
4 I don't understand / am not understanding this word.
5 Do you know / Are you knowing my teacher?

Write the correct form of the verb in (brackets).

What time _do you want_ (want) to meet me tonight?

Bruno _is driving_ (drive) to work today.

1 They _____ (not / like) watching horror films.
2 The students _____ (need) new dictionaries.
3 The children usually _____ (do) their homework in the evening.
4 _____ (you / understand) what the teacher is saying?
5 What _____ (you / want) for lunch?
6 We _____ (not / go) for a drink after work tonight.
7 He _____ (not / walk) to school today because it's raining.
8 When _____ (need) your book?

natural English phoning a friend

7 Put the telephone conversation in order.

Sunita Hello?
Sally   ___a___
Sunita ___1___
Sally   ___2___
Sunita ___3___
Sally   ___4___
Sunita ___5___
Sally   ___6___
Sunita ___7___
Sally   ___8___ . Bye.

a ~~Oh hi. Is that Sunita?~~
b Hi Sally. What's the matter?
c Yes, please.
d Okay, see you in about 15 minutes.
e Yeah, it is.
f Hi, it's Sally.
g Thanks a lot, Sunita.
h Well, I need some help with my homework.
i Shall I come to your flat?

natural English telephone introductions

8 Complete the conversation with a suitable word. There may be more than one possible answer.

R = receptionist; **E** = Elizabeth

R Good morning, International English Learning Centre.

E Good morning. _Could / Can_ _____ I speak to Jenny Jones, please?

R Who's ¹_____ , please?

E My ²_____ 's Elizabeth Richardson. I work at the university.

R Just a minute … I'm sorry, Jenny's teaching at the moment. Would you like to leave a ³_____ ?

E Yes, please. Could you ask Jenny to ⁴_____ me?

R Certainly, what's your ⁵_____ ?

E My office number is 678945 and the best time to call is after lunch.

R Okay, so that's Elizabeth Richardson, telephone number 678945, and you want Jenny to call after lunch.

E That's right. Thanks very much.

write it!

Look at the telephone conversation in exercise 8. Write the message for Jenny Jones. Include the following:

caller's name   caller's phone number   message

natural English showing you (don't) understand

9 Underline the phrases that Javier uses to show that he understands / doesn't understand.

M = Michelle; **J** = Javier

M What do you fancy doing today?
J Sorry?
M What do you want to do?
J Ah! OK. Well, I have to buy some presents for my family.
M You should go to Harrods.
J Pardon? Who is Harry?
M Harrods. It's a big department store.
J Oh yes, Harrods. How do I get there?
M By train and tube.
J Sorry, what's a 'tube'?
M It's like the metro in Barcelona.
J Oh, I see.
M Look here's a map. Take the train to Richmond, get on the District line tube, change at Earl's Court and get the Piccadilly Line tube to Knightsbridge.
J Er,… Could you repeat that?
M Don't worry, I can take you.

pronunciation consonant groups

10 Underline the words that begin with two consonant sounds. Say the words.

He <u>skis</u> in winter.

1 How do you spell your name?
2 Her cat sleeps all day.
3 I need some new clothes for work.
4 We travel a lot.
5 Did you have breakfast?

Tick (✓) when you've done these sections.

natural English
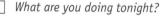
- [ ] *What are you doing tonight?*
- [ ] *Do you ever ...?*
- [ ] inviting and responding
- [ ] making plans together

grammar
- [ ] *be going to* + verb
- [ ] *might* + verb

vocabulary
- [ ] verb + preposition
- [ ] kinds of film

 **a new life**

grammar *be going to* + verb; *might* /maɪt/ + verb

NAME: **Sally Ferndale**

Age: 18
Leaves: March 6th
How long: 6 months
Where: Ecuador
Work: four months teaching English to 6–8 years olds in Quito
Plans: travel around South America, learn Spanish, learn salsa
After gap year: go to university

NAME: **Joe Perry**

Age: 22
Leaves: January 27th
How long: 12 months
Where: France, Germany, Czech Republic, Poland, Russia, China, Italy, Spain, Portugal
Work: no
Plans: learn Russian and Chinese
After gap year: find a job

1 Are the sentences true ✓ or false ✗ ?

Joe's going to travel for one year. ✓

1 Joe and Sally are going to learn a foreign language.
2 Sally's going to work with children.
3 Sally's going to visit Spain.
4 Sally is going to dance.
5 Joe and Sally are going to work abroad.
6 Joe and Sally are going to visit South America.
7 Joe's going to study at university after his gap year.
8 Sally's going to travel for six months.

Hi Mum! Hi Dad!

It's Day 10 of my trip and I'm in Paris. It's great here! I met somebody called Tom on the train yesterday, and he's on a gap year too. We're staying in a hotel near the city centre.

Tonight we're going to go up the Eiffel Tower, then walk or take the metro to the Latin Quarter. Tomorrow I want to go to Versailles but it might be closed on Mondays.

On Tuesday Tom and I have to get up very early to catch the train to Strasbourg. We've booked a room at the hostel there. After Strasbourg, I'm not sure; I want to go to Berlin but Tom has a friend in Munich and he says we can stay there.

Anyway, I hope you're OK.

Bye for now

Joe xx

natural English *What are you doing tonight?*

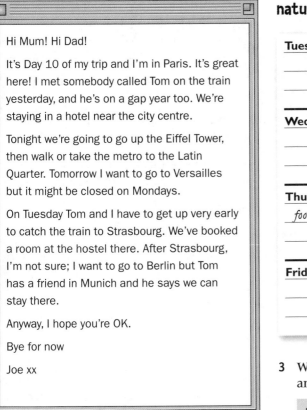

Tuesday		Saturday
—		*?skiing*
Wednesday		**Sunday**
cinema (Pirates of the Caribbean) Luis & Ana		*?skiing*
Thursday		**Monday**
football – sports centre		*Russian lesson*
		? drink with Luis
Friday		
take car ? garage		
buy new jumper		

2 Read the text. Write *might* or *is / are going to*.

Joe and Tom *might* walk to the Latin Quarter.

1 Joe _____ visit Versailles on Monday.

2 Joe _____ catch a train on Tuesday.

3 Joe _____ stay in a hostel in Strasbourg.

4 Tom _____ travel to Strasbourg with Joe.

5 Joe _____ travel to Munich.

3 Write questions about Javier's plans. Use *What are you doing …?* and the phrases in the box.

~~this Friday~~	next Monday	~~tonight~~
at the weekend	tomorrow	the day after tomorrow

A *What are you doing tonight?*

B Not much, I'm really tired and I don't want go out.

1 A _____

   B I'm going to the cinema with a couple of my friends.

2 A _____

   B Oh, I always play football at the sports centre on Thursdays.

3 A _____

   B I'm taking the car to the garage and going shopping for clothes.

4 A _____

   B I'm not sure. I might go skiing.

5 A _____

   B I've got a Russian lesson and I might go for a drink with Luis.

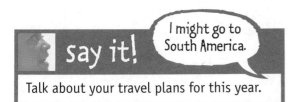

I might go to South America.

say it!

Talk about your travel plans for this year.

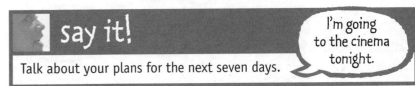

I'm going to the cinema tonight.

say it!

Talk about your plans for the next seven days.

wordbooster

verb + preposition

4 Match the beginnings and endings of the sentences.

How long did you have to wait
1 I spoke
2 Carlos didn't agree
3 I can't go out tonight. I have to look
4 Did you speak
5 Elena spent all of her money
6 We paid € 2,000
7 Are you thinking
8 Do you want to listen

a about the exam?
b on new clothes for her children.
c to some music?
d to Jim yesterday evening.
e for the train tickets.
f for the bus this morning?
g after my little brother.
h with the teacher's ideas.
i to Tomas yesterday?

test yourself!

Cover a to i in exercise 4.
Complete sentences 1 to 8 using your own words.

natural English   *Do you ever ...?*

5 Order the words to make questions.

play / Do / basketball / ever / you ?
Do you ever play basketball?

1 the / you / Do / go / cinema / in / ever / the / to / afternoon ?

_____

2 you / ever / action / watch / Do / films ?

_____

3 read / Does / horror / she / ever / stories ?

_____

4 Do / by / taxi / travel / they / ever ?

_____

5 he / Does / watch / ever / cartoons ?

_____

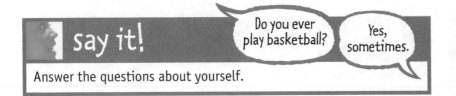

say it!

Answer the questions about yourself.

Do you ever play basketball?

Yes, sometimes.

kinds of film

think back!

Remember five more kinds of film. *comedy*

6 Find eight kinds of film in the puzzle. Complete the words.

comedy

1 r _____ comedy
2 m _____
3 w _____ film
4 t _____
5 w _____
6 c _____
7 a _____ film
8 h _____ film

R	O	M	A	N	T	I	C	H	A	B
N	M	U	Y	C	Z	X	A	S	C	A
C	I	S	D	T	T	R	R	C	T	B
O	K	I	A	X	H	L	T	F	I	H
M	E	C	P	L	R	L	O	H	O	O
E	L	A	Q	L	I	P	O	N	N	R
D	L	L	T	H	L	I	N	L	E	R
Y	O	A	E	L	L	T	L	W	G	R
C	P	T	R	T	E	H	X	A	J	O
W	E	S	T	E	R	N	A	R	O	R

say it!

What kinds of film do you enjoy / not enjoy?

how to ...invite someone

natural English inviting and responding

7 Complete the conversation using the phrases in the box.

What's it about	Shall I buy	Where's it on	I'm a bit busy
what are you doing	Do you want	Would you like to	What's on
How about you	~~do you want to~~		

Ana Jemma, *do you want to* _____ come to the cinema tonight?

Jemma Sorry, 1_____ tonight.

Ana Luis, 2_____ after work?

Luis Nothing. Why?

Ana 3_____ to go and see a film?

Luis 4_____ ?

Ana *Hide and Seek*; it's the new Robert De Niro film.

Luis 5_____ ?

Ana It's a horror film.

Luis Yeah, OK. 6_____ ?

Ana The big Multiplex cinema.

Luis 7_____ go for a meal first? There's a Spanish restaurant near the Multiplex.

Ana Yes, great.

Luis 8_____ some tickets on the Internet?

Ana Good idea.

<u>Underline</u> the phrases that Ana, Luis, and Jemma use to respond to invitations.

write it!

Write an e-mail to your friend. Invite him / her to go for a drink.

natural English making plans together

8 Match the questions and responses.

What shall we do at the weekend? _d_

1 Good idea. Where shall we go? ____

2 OK. How shall we get there? ____

3 Fine. Where shall we meet? ____

4 Yes, OK. When shall we meet? ____

5 Yes. What shall we take? ____

a By train.

b How about 9.00?

c Some sandwiches and something to drink.

d How about a picnic?

e To the beach at Brighton?

f At the station?

9 Put the telephone conversation in order.

a Fine. What time?
b How about the restaurant?
c ~~Where shall we meet tomorrow night?~~
d Yeah, OK.
e At 6.00?
f Right, so that's 6.00 at the restaurant.

Ana Hello.

Luis Hi, Ana. It's Luis.

Ana Oh, hi Luis.

Luis I forgot to ask. _c_ ___

Ana 1 ____

Luis 2 ____

Ana 3 ____

Luis 4 ____

Ana 5 ____ . See you tomorrow.

Luis Bye, Ana.

Ana Bye.

fourteen

Tick (✓) when you've done these sections.

natural English
- [ ] *How many times …?*
- [ ] *have a + adjective + noun*

grammar
- [ ] present perfect (experience)
- [ ] present perfect and past simple

vocabulary
- [ ] opposites
- [ ] feelings
- [ ] fixed phrases

that's incredible!

natural English *How many times …?*

1 Do the quiz. How adventurous are you?

How many times in the last ten years have you …	A three or more times	B twice	C once	D never
changed your job?				
moved town / city?				
travelled to another country?				
learned to do something new?				
made a new friend?				
Your score	As = 4	Bs = 3	Cs = 2	Ds = 1

1– 5 *Wake up!*

6–10 *Leave the house and get to know the world.*

11–15 *Don't stop! There's lots more to see and do.*

16–20 *That's incredible! When do you sleep?*

say it!

Answer the quiz questions.

I've made lots of new friends.

grammar present perfect (experience)

2 Read the text and the list.

Teachers Gary Banks and his wife, Tanya, saw a TV programme about the fifty most popular things that people wanted to do before they died. Gary and Tanya wrote a list of things that they want to do before they die. So far, they have done five of the things on the list.

Bungee jumping in New Zealand

THINGS TO DO BEFORE WE DIE!

– fly a hot air balloon in South Africa ✓ (July '04)

– see the pyramids in Egypt

– visit Paris and have dinner
  at the Eiffel Tower restaurant ✓ (May '05)

– do a bungee jump in New Zealand ✓ (Dec '04)

– travel on the Orient Express train

– visit Disneyland in the USA

– ride a camel in Tunisia ✓ (July '04)

– sail a boat around the world

– write a book about our adventures

– swim with sharks in Australia ✓ (Aug '05)

Are the statements true ✓ or false ✗?

They've done half of the things on their list. ✓

1 They've eaten in a restaurant in Paris.
2 They haven't written a book.
3 They haven't swum with sharks.
4 They've been to Egypt.
5 They haven't flown a hot air balloon.

write it!

Write a list of ten things that you haven't done but want to do before you die.

I haven't been in an aeroplane.

grammar present perfect and past simple

3 <u>Underline</u> the correct form.

Naila Did you ever go / <u>Have you ever been</u> to New Zealand?

Jack Yes, I [1] did / have.

Naila When [2] did you go / have you been?

Jack Last summer. [3] Did you ever go / Have you ever been?

Naila No. My sister [4] went / has been there last year but I [5] didn't go / haven't been with her.

Jack Why not?

Naila I [6] didn't have / haven't had any money.

Jack Well, it's a great place to go and the people are very friendly.

Naila Where [7] did you stay / have you stayed?

Jack In hostels mostly, but sometimes I [8] stayed / have stayed with friends.

Naila [9] Did you do / Have you done anything exciting when you were there?

Jack Well, I [10] did / 've done a bungee jump from a bridge.

Naila That's amazing!

wordbooster

opposites

4 Order the letters to make verbs or adverbs.

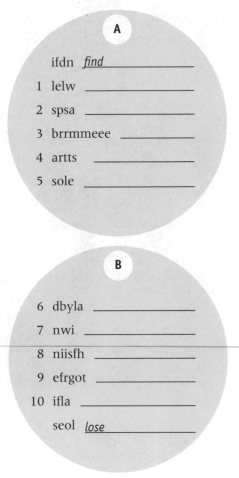

A

ifdn _find_

1 lelw _____

2 spsa _____

3 brrmmeee _____

4 artts _____

5 sole _____

B

6 dbyla _____

7 nwi _____

8 niisfh _____

9 efrgot _____

10 ifla _____

seol _lose_

5 Match the words (in A) with their opposites (in B).

find/lose _____

1 _____

2 _____

3 _____

4 _____

5 _____

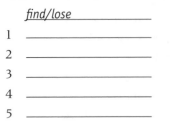

test yourself!

Cover circle A. Say the opposites of the words in circle B.

think back!

Remember five more words to describe feelings. _embarrassed_

feelings

6 Complete the e-mail. Use the words in the box. There are two extra words.

excited	frightened	~~pleased~~	nervous
sad	surprised	embarrassed	angry

Hi Sue!

Well, I've finally finished! Yesterday was my last day teaching at the college. I'm really _pleased_ _____ that I don't have to go back but I felt quite ¹_____ when I said goodbye to my students. They gave me a Good Luck card and some lovely flowers.

I think my new job is going to be great! I am very ²_____ about starting next week. I was quite ³_____ when they gave me the job because my interview wasn't very good. I was really ⁴_____ because I got lost and arrived late!

Next week I'm going to Warsaw for a meeting. I'm quite ⁵_____ because the meeting's going to be in Polish. I hope I can understand everyone.

Well, I better go. I've got lots to do before Monday.

Take care,

Maria xx

how to ... say what you feel

vocabulary fixed phrases

7 Tick ✓ the best response.

1 They didn't offer me the job.
   a Congratulations!
   b Good luck!
   c That's a shame! ✓

2 I'm really sorry. I've broken your glass.
   a Thanks a lot.
   b Don't worry.
   c Have a good time.

3 I've won the lottery!
   a What a shame!
   b I'm really sorry.
   c Congratulations!

4 We got you this book for your birthday.
   a Thanks a lot.
   b Good luck!
   c Congratulations!

5 I've got an exam in the morning.
   a Have a good time.
   b That's great.
   c Good luck!

6 We're going on holiday next week.
   a I'm really sorry.
   b Have a good time.
   c That's a shame.

natural English
have a + adjective + noun

8 Underline the correct phrase.

   A Sandra, I'm going to work now.
   B Have a nice holiday. / Have a nice day.

1 A We're going skiing next week.
   B Well, have a great time! / have a nice day!

2 A I'm going to Spain tomorrow.
   B Have a nice evening! / Have a lovely holiday!
   A Thanks!

3 A I'm going out for a meal with Andy after work.
   B Have a good weekend. / Have a nice evening.

4 A Well, it's Friday and it's 5 o'clock so I'm going home! See you on Monday.
   B Have a good weekend. / Have a nice day.
   A Thanks! You too!

5 A We're going to have a picnic on Sunday.
   B Have a nice evening. / Have a lovely day.

pronunciation linking

9 Mark the linked sounds.

   I've never been in love.

1 I've run a marathon.
2 I've visited Italy twice.
3 I've never lived alone.
4 I've been in hospital several times.
5 I've never met anyone famous.
6 I've driven a Ferrari.
7 I've written a book.
8 I've learned a lot of English!

say it!

Cover the reponses (a, b, and c) in exercise 7.
Respond to sentences 1 to 6.

say it!

Say the sentences that are true for you.

unit one

1
1 Hi, my name's Tomás.
2 Nice to meet you.
3 Hello, I'm Sandro.
4 Hello, my name's Rebecca.
5 Nice to meet you, Rebecca.

2
1 ✗   5 ✗
2 ✓   6 ✓
3 ✗   7 ✗
4 ✗   8 ✓

say it!
1 Is Katia from Barcelona?
   No, she isn't.
2 Is Katia married?
   No, she isn't.
3 Is Tomás from Poland?
   No, he isn't.
4 Is Tomás single?
   No, he isn't.
5 Is Katia a doctor?
   Yes, she is.
6 Is Tomás from Spain?
   Yes, he is.
7 Is Tomás forty?
   Yes, he is.
8 Is Katia thirty?
   Yes, she is.

3
L A W Y E R
S H O P A S S I S T A N T
P O L I C E O F F I C E R
A C T O R
B U S I N E S S M A N
J O U R N A L I S T

4
1 an
2 a
3 a
4 an
5 an

5
2 forty-eight
3 thirteen
4 twenty-one
5 sixty-seven
6 fifty-nine

say it! *students' own answers*

6
1 's Thai
2 're German
3 's French
4 's Japanese
5 're Polish
6 's Argentinian / Argentine
7 's Italian
8 're Chinese

eyg
1 the   5 the
2 –   6 –
3 –   7 –
4 the   8 the

1 Budapest is in ~~the~~ Hungary.
2 Rick is from **the** United States.
3 ✓
4 ✓
5 London is in **the** United Kingdom.

7
1 How
2 Fine / Very well
3 you
4 Very
5 thanks

8
1 i   5 b
2 e   6 h
3 c   7 a
4 d   8 f

9
1 orange
2 diet
3 mineral
4 red
5 black

10
1 Would you like a glass of wine?
2 Would you like tea with lemon?
3 Yes, a diet cola, please.
4 Would you like a hot chocolate?
5 Yes, a mineral water, please.

say it!
Would you like …
a mineral water?
a black coffee?
a glass of orange juice?
a diet cola?

eyv

	coffee	wine	fruit juice	cola	hot chocolate
glass		✓	✓	✓	
1 **bottle**		✓		✓	
2 **can**				✓	
3 **mug**	✓				✓
4 **carton**		✓	✓		
5 **cup**	✓				(✓)

1 glass
2 bottles
3 carton
4 mug
5 cans

11 /eɪ/ a, h, j, k
/iː/ b, c, d, e, g, t, v
/aɪ/ i, y
/e/ f, l, m, n, s, x
and z (in Br Eng)
/uː/ q, u, w
letters not in the circles are
o and r

say it! *students' own answers*

write it! *students' own answers*

12 1 a
2 b
3 a
4 b
5 a

unit two

1
1 computer
2 laptop
3 camera
4 CD player
5 printer
laptop is not in the puzzle

M B Y L C T A S A C O
X O O P L W H I I D L
P Z B R E E Y T R P U
E C W I Q Q U U H L M
C U J N L B K V W A Y
A H I T I E O P O Y X
M N B E B R P H O E E
E W Q R Q Q D H P R E
R I I A Y E C C B O
A D F E I L O S S N P
A C O M P U T E R B E

say it! pronunciation
compu**t**er, prin**t**er, pla**y**er
ca**m**era, **m**obile **ph**one, **l**aptop
students' own answers

2
1 things
2 thing
3 things
4 thing
5 things

3
1 Have   6 Has
2 haven't   7 has
3 Has   8 Have
4 has   9 have / 've
5 haven't   10 have

4
1 expensive
2 CD players
3 necessary
4 mobile phones
5 useful

write it! *students' own answers*

eyv
1 e   5 g
2 b   6 d
3 f   7 a
4 i   8 c

eyg
1 computers   5 boxes
2 women   6 country
3 class   7 desks
4 person   8 nationalities

eyg
1 Javier has got two English ~~dictionarys~~ dictionaries.
2 ✓
3 How many ~~persons~~ people are in your class?
4 Three ~~glass~~ glasses of white wine, please.
5 Guilia and Emilio have got four ~~childrens~~ children.
6 The ~~womans~~ women at the party are from Brazil.
7 ✓
8 I think the new ~~computeres~~ computers are great.

5
2 magazine   6 dictionary
3 lighter   7 notebook
4 key   8 newspaper
5 travel card 9 briefcase

say it! *students' own answers*

6
1 Where is Brigitte's calculator?
2 Gianni's homework is difficult.
3 Brad is Julia's boyfriend.
4 Are they Simon's coursebooks?
5 Maria's new bag is yellow.

7 *(see below)*

say it! pronunciation
terrible, different, similar,
boring, interesting, noisy,
quiet, dangerous, expensive
students' own answers

8 1 f   2 c   3 b   4 a   5 e

say it! *possible answers*
Can I borrow / look at your dictionary?
Can you turn off the fan?
Can I turn on the light?
Can you help me?

9
1 this is   5 Those are
2 that's   6 This is
3 those   7 these
4 Is that   8 that's

10 1 e   2 b   3 a   4 f   5 d

11 1 a ●●
2 b ●●●
3 f ●
4 c ●●●
5 d ●●

7
Crossword:
3 across: I N T E R E S T I N G
1 down: G R E A T
2 down: S M I L A ... (SMILING)
5 across: D A N G E R O U S
4 down: Q U I E T
6 across: E X P E N S I V E

unit three

1
1 work
2 take
3 doesn't work
4 go out
5 play
6 live
7 work
8 don't go out
9 listen to
10 play

write it! *students' own answers*

2
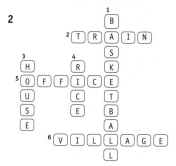

3
1 I drive A lot.
2 They eat a lot OF Chinese food.
3 We stay at home a LOT.
4 They GO OUT a lot.
5 You drink a lot of COFFEE.

4
1 What's your address?
  c 124 Elm Street
2 Where do you work?
  f at the university
3 What do you teach?
  a French
4 When do you leave home?
  e 7.30 a.m.
5 How do you get to work?
  d by car

5
2 drive
3 the train
4 cycle
5 the bus
6 car

say it! *students' own answers*

6
1 cooking
2 driving
3 playing
4 shopping
5 skiing
6 travelling
7 dancing
8 sightseeing

7

say it! *students' own answers*

8
1 It's quarter to four.
2 Excuse me, have you got the time?
3 Sorry, no I haven't.
4 Have you got the time, please?
5 Yes, it's twenty-five past three.

9
1 don't like
2 quite like
3 really like
4 really like
5 quite like
6 hate
7 quite like
8 don't like
9 hate
10 really like

say it! *students' own answers*

10
1 drives
2 lives
3 listens
4 studies
5 reads
6 eats
7 drinks
8 plays

11
1 Yes, she does.
2 No, she doesn't.
3 No, she doesn't.
4 Yes, she does.
5 No, she doesn't.

eyv
1 tennis court
2 dance studio
3 swimming pool
4 fitness room
5 changing room

1 studio
2 fitness room
3 courts
4 pool
5 court

eyg
1 We love skiing but we hate swimming.
2 They drink tea and coffee.
3 I don't like skiing because it's dangerous.
4 He plays football but he doesn't play basketball.
5 I like my room because it's quiet.
6 I don't like this exercise because it's difficult.
7 Mona speaks Italian and Russian.
8 Enrique likes sightseeing and shopping.

say it! *students' own answers*

unit four

1
1 leaves
2 gets
3 has
4 reads
5 gets
6 has
7 watches
8 goes

say it! *students' own answers*

eyv
1 e
2 b
3 a
4 d
5 f

say it! *students' own answers*

2
1 George sleeps about nine hours a night.
2 Magda works about seven hours a day.
3 Miguel studies English about two hours a week.
4 John and Kay watch TV about four hours a night.
5 Javier plays computer games about one hour a day.

eyg
1 Have a bath.
2 Take the bus.
3 Clean the bathroom.
4 Make your beds.
5 Go to bed.

3
b I never read adventure stories.
c I sometimes read sports magazines.
d I usually read love stories.
e I often read on the bus.
f I hardly ever buy books.

4
1 c
2 e
3 f
4 d
5 b

say it! *students' own answers*

5
1 autumn
2 months
3 summer
4 March
5 August

6
1 at
2 on
3 in
4 at
5 on
6 on
7 during
8 at

say it!
on Wednesday, at 2 p.m., on January 21st, at the weekend, during the week, in March, at the moment, in the winter, between 2.30 and 3.30

7
1 Mike
2 Harry
3 Sylvia
4 Dave
5 John
6 Camilla
7 Jenny
8 James
9 Rachel
10 Rosie

8
1 b (No, I haven't.)
2 a (Yes, I've got two.)
3 d (Yes, I've got one brother and two sisters.)
4 f (Yes, I've got two nephews and two nieces.)
5 c (Yes, I've got three.)

9
1 Our
2 our
3 her
4 his
5 Their
6 my
7 her
8 its

write it! *students' own answer*

10
1 Belinda / John
2 Belinda / Patricia
3 Patricia / Jamie
4 Bob / Belinda
5 Jamie / Patricia

11 /θ/ birthday, month, fifth, thanks
/ð/ together, their, the, brother

unit five

1 1 toast
2 sausage
3 bacon
4 cheese / ham
5 cereal
6 bread / honey
7 coffee
8 juice

2 1 They always have cereal.
2 He often has sandwiches.
3 I never have lunch.
4 We sometimes have Indian food.
5 She usually has pasta.

say it! *students' own answers*

think back!

cheese (u)   apple (c)
sandwich (c)   honey (u)
sausage (c)   tea (u)

3 1 a
2 a
3 b
4 b
5 a

4 1 ~~any~~ / a
2 ~~any~~ / some
3 ~~a~~ / some
4 ~~a~~ / some
5 ~~some~~ / any

5 1 cheap
2 uncomfortable
3 clean
4 excellent
5 slow

write it! *students' own answers*

6 2 chicken
3 steak
4 mushroom
5 onion
6 chocolate
7 peas
8 fish
9 tomato

```
P O T A T O T S S H S
O P H L P Q M T P P T
C W X I M K U B E L E
H D P F F U S I A E A
I N R R O S H V S T K
C U U U N L R P X J H
K S S A I Z O A Z I U
E D Y P N O M M S V H
I K U L B M N F I S H
O T O M A T O C F C M
```

say it! *students' own answers*

eyg

2 some
3 some
4 a
5 some
6 some

7 1 coffee
2 ice-cream
3 sandwich
4 wine
5 juice

eyv

1 strawberry   1 dairy
2 grapes   2 grapes
3 bananas   3 meat
4 pepper   4 carrots
5 carrot   5 banana
6 sweetcorn
7 cream
8 yoghurt
9 pork chop
10 turkey

8 1 can
2 can't
3 can't
4 can't
5 can't
6 can
7 can
8 can

9 1 a
2 h
3 f
4 d
5 e
6 i
7 g
8 j
9 b
10 c

say it! *students' own answers*

10 1 some more
2 some more
3 another
4 some more
5 another

say it! *students' own answers*

unit six

1 1 Church
2 Bridge
3 Museum
4 Market
5 Castle

eyv

2 d   2 guidebook
3 b   3 walking shoes
4 a   4 sunglasses
5 f   5 streetmap
6 c   6 backpack

say it! *students' own answers*

2 1 The tickets was / <u>were</u> very expensive.
2 We was / <u>were</u> at the tourist office at 8 a.m. but our bus <u>was</u> / were late.
3 The bus <u>was</u> / were cold and the seats was / <u>were</u> uncomfortable.
4 The driver <u>wasn't</u> / weren't very friendly.
5 The tour guide <u>was</u> / were very young and he <u>was</u> / were boring.
6 The museum and the castle was / <u>were</u> closed.
7 The food at the restaurant <u>was</u> / were awful.
8 We was / <u>were</u> very tired at the end of the day.

3 1 No, they weren't.
2 Yes, it was.
3 No, he wasn't.
4 Yes, it was.
5 Yes, they were.

4 *see quiz answers underneath quiz*
1 The Coliseum and the Vatican are both in Rome.
2 China and Thailand are both Asian countries.
3 The White House and Camp David are both homes of the US President.
4 The Nile and the Amazon are both rivers.
5 Warsaw and Kraków are both cities in Poland.

5 1 Our bus was late yesterday morning.
2 I was tired last night.
3 We were at the museum a few days ago.
4 Roger was in Thailand in 2001.
5 It was my birthday ten days ago.

say it! *students' own answers*

6 1 cleans
2 meet
3 go
4 stays
5 goes out
6 do
7 play
8 washes

7 1 Lovely
2 nice
3 boring
4 terrible
5 interesting

write it! *students' own answers*

8 1 watched
2 bought
3 decided
4 met
5 got up
6 wanted
7 cleaned
8 liked
9 went
10 stayed

9 1 decided
2 bought
3 stayed
4 cleaned
5 watched
6 liked
7 had
8 got up
9 went
10 met

eyg

1 before
2 after
3 after
4 before
5 after

10 1 That
2 was
3 worry
4 sorry
5 Don't

say it! *students' own answers*

11 1 a coursebook / boring
2 b talk / sport
3 b church / were
4 b shopping / got
5 a coffee / Australia

unit seven

1
1 was born
2 grew up
3 left
4 went
5 worked
6 became
7 got married
8 had

write it! *students' own answers*

2
1 He didn't go to university.
2 He didn't work in a gym.
3 He didn't go to America in 1966.
4 He didn't act in his first American film in 1970.
5 He didn't get married in 1986.

3
1 d
2 e
3 b
4 c
5 a

4
1 ✗
2 ✓
3 ✗
4 ✓
5 ✗

say it! *students' own answers*

5
2 quite tall
3 very tall
4 quite short
5 very short
6 short

6
1 medium
2 dark
3 short
4 beard
5 moustache
6 tall
7 blonde
8 looking

say it! *students' own answers*

7

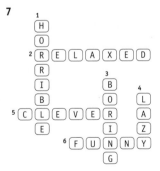

eyv
1 thin (A)
2 funny (C)
3 boring (C)
4 blonde (A)
5 clever (C)
6 fat (A)
7 nice (C)
8 relaxed (C)

1 dull
2 pretty
3 calm
4 plump
5 lovely
6 amusing
7 thin
8 blonde

8
1 you
2 me
3 them
4 him
5 him
6 her
7 us
8 it

9
1 friendly
2 Boring
3 clever
4 lazy
5 nice

say it! *students' own answers*

eyg
1 yours
2 hers
3 his
4 ours
5 theirs

1 hers
2 mine
3 ours
4 theirs
5 mine
6 yours
7 his
8 his
9 theirs
10 hers

10
1 When did you last eat french fries?
2 When was the last time you washed your car?
3 When did you last speak English?
4 When did you last play football?
5 When was the last time you travelled by train?

say it! *students' own answers*

unit eight

1
2 d
3 b
4 a
5 c
6 f

eyv
1 d
2 a
3 f
4 c
5 b

1 return
2 platform
3 passengers
4 ticket office
5 timetable

2
1 How many days did you stay (in the hotel) in Cairo?
2 How many hours were you on the train?
3 How much food did you have on the train?
4 How much money did you take?
5 How much jewellery did you buy?

say it!
1 a few
2 a lot
3 none
4 quite a lot
5 a lot

3
2 car park
3 train station
4 museum
5 cinema
6 school
7 restaurant
8 statue
9 hotel

write it! *students' own answers*

4
1 took
2 went
3 come
4 goes
5 take
6 brought
7 bring
8 came

5
1 isn't
2 a
3 are
4 a
5 aren't

6
1 are there
2 where
3 sorry
4 there isn't
5 on the

7
1 e
2 f
3 b
4 c
5 d

say it! *possible answers*
book cupboard: Turn left and go along the corridor, then turn right. It's the second door on your right.
Spanish department: Turn left and go along the corridor, then turn right. It's the second door on your left.
stairs: Turn left and go along the corridor, then turn right. Go to the end of the corridor, turn right, and it's the first door on your right.
coffee room: Turn right and it's the first door on your right.
lecture room: Turn left and go along the corridor, then turn right. It's the first door on your right.

eyg
1 b
2 i
3 h
4 d
5 f
6 a
7 e
8 g

8
1 journalist
2 sausages
3 Russia
4 chef
5 fish
6 China
7 teacher
8 chips

1
1 F
2 T
3 T
4 T
5 F
6 F
7 F
8 F

2
1 No, you don't.
2 Yes, you do.
3 No, you don't.
4 No, you don't.
5 No, you don't.

3
1 can't
2 can
3 can
4 can't
5 can't

say it! *students' own answers*

eyg
1 does
2 was
3 can
4 do
5 didn't
6 has
7 are
8 has

4
1 a
2 f
3 e
4 b
5 c

say it! *students' own answers*

5
1 f
2 b
3 a
4 e
5 c

6
1 f
2 a
3 e
4 d
5 b

7
1 d
2 h
3 e
4 c
5 b
6 i
7 a
8 f

8

	yotel	formule 1	Hotel HK
double room	✓	✓	✓
en-suite rooms	✓	✗	✓
bath	✗	✗	✓
shower	✓	✓	✓
Internet access	✓	✗	✓
parking	✗	✓	✓
swimming pool	✗	✗	✓
gym	✗	✗	✓
restaurant	✗	✗	✓
bar	✗	✗	✓
breakfast included in price	✗	✗	✓

say it! *students' own answers*

9
1 Has the hotel got a pool?
2 Has it got a restaurant?
3 Is there a gym?
4 Is breakfast included in the price?
5 Are there any rooms available?

eyv
1 g   1 hangers
2 i   2 fan
3 d   3 pillows
4 f   4 kettle
5 c   5 balcony
6 h
7 e
8 a

10
1 R
2 W
3 W
4 R
5 R
6 W
7 R
8 R

say it! *students' own answers*

11
1 c
2 d
3 f
4 b
5 a

1

3
1 can't
2 can't
3 can
4 can't
5 can

4
1 a
2 b
3 a
4 b
5 b

say it! *students' own answers*

5
2 hair
3 mouth
4 stomach
5 eyes
6 teeth
7 shoulder
8 thumb
9 fingers

6
1 b
2 c
3 a
4 c
5 b

write it! *students' own answers*

eyv
1 backache   1 toothache
2 toothache   2 headache
3 headache   3 backache
4 earache   4 neckache
5 stomachache   5 earache

say it! *students' own answers*

7
1 I think it's better to stop smoking.
2 I think it's better to ask the teacher.
3 I think it's better to take the train.
4 I think it's better to look at the map.
5 I think it's better to buy a new TV.

8
1 anyone
2 no-one
3 nothing
4 anyone
5 anyone
6 something
7 Someone
8 anything

9
1 ✓
2 *something* / ~~anything~~
3 *anything* / ~~nothing~~
4 *nothing* / ~~something~~
5 *anything* / ~~nothing~~

10
1 c
2 e
3 d
4 b
5 a

say it! *students' own answers*

eyg
1 anywhere
2 somewhere
3 nowhere
4 ~~anywhere~~
5 somewhere
6 nowhere
7 somewhere
8 somewhere
9 nowhere
10 somewhere

11
1 house
2 Could / spoon
3 toothache
4 foot
5 Would
6 countries
7 about
8 cousin

mouth /aʊ/	hours, about, house
group /uː/	toothache, spoon, soup
double /ʌ/	couple, countries, cousin
took /ʊ/	foot, could, would

unit eleven

1 Sam (in any order)
1 more expensive
2 easier
3 quieter
4 better
5 more interesting

Michael (in any order)
6 worse
7 more boring
8 more difficult
9 cheaper
10 noisier

2 1 c, 2 f, 3 b, 4 a, 5 d

say it! *students' own answers*

3 1 more dangerous
2 colder
3 older
4 healthier
5 more common

4 1 I agree.
2 I'm not sure.
3 It depends.
4 I'm not so sure.
5 I don't agree.

say it! *students' own answers*

eyv
1 flight   1 tour
2 cruise   2 drive
3 drive   3 flight
4 tour   4 drive
5 excursion   5 excursion
               6 cruise

say it! *students' own answers*

5

1 aspirin
2 perfume
3 lamb
4 chair
5 cassettes
6 stamps
7 shirt
8 cakes

6 1 What did you get at the baker's?
2 I got this shirt in Milan.
3 Where can I get some envelopes?
4 We have to get some chairs.
5 Where did you get that bag?

7 1 b
2 a
3 b
4 c
5 a
6 c
7 b
8 a

8 1 f
2 e
3 d
4 a
5 b

9 1 friendliest
2 most comfortable
3 longest
4 most beautiful
5 most famous
6 cheapest
7 nicest
8 best

write it! *students' own answers*

10 1 Sydney has the hottest summers.
2 Sydney is the biggest city.
3 Sydney is the newest city.
4 Moscow has the coldest winters.
5 Moscow has the most people.
6 Reyjavik is the smallest city.
7 Reyjavik has the coldest summers.
8 Reyjavik has the fewest people.

say it! *students' own answers*

eyg
1 too modern
2 too small
3 too difficult
4 too hot
5 too noisy
6 too late
7 too tired
8 too big

unit twelve

1 1 f
2 a
3 e
4 d
5 c

say it! *students' own answers*

2 2 Naila
3 Carlos
4 Rebecca
5 Chang
6 Maria
7 Gemma
8 Kevin
9 John

3 1 I am talking to my friends.
2 Are Tomas and Luis working today?
3 They aren't smoking.
4 She's listening to her CDs.
5 What's she wearing?
6 We aren't playing computer games.
7 What are those students studying?
8 John and Kevin are talking.

say it! *students' own answers*

4 2 dress
3 hat
4 skirt
5 jeans
6 jacket
7 shirt
8 trousers
9 trainers

```
                    9
        ¹B O O T S
           ²D R E S S
          ³H A T
         ⁴S K I R T
       ⁵J E A N S
      ⁶J A C K E T
        ⁷S H I R T
     ⁸T R O U S E R S
```

say it! *students' own answers*

5 1 b
2 a
3 b
4 a
5 c

eyv
1 c   1 e
2 f   2 a
3 d   3 c
4 b   4 d
5 a   5 f

say it! *students' own answers*

6 1 'm texting
2 play
3 'm practising
4 Does it take
5 's ringing
6 'm having
7 go
8 meet
9 's working
10 does your mum do

eyg
1 Do you like
2 wants
3 Does she need
4 I don't understand
5 Do you know

1 don't like
2 need
3 do
4 Do you understand
5 do you want
6 aren't going
7 isn't walking
8 do you need

7 1 e
2 f
3 b
4 h
5 i
6 c
7 d
8 g

8 1 calling / speaking
2 name
3 message
4 phone / ring / call
5 number

write it! *students' own answers*

9 understands:
Ah, OK. Oh yes. Oh, I see.
doesn't understand:
Pardon? Sorry? Could you repeat that?

10 1 spell
2 sleeps
3 clothes
4 travel
5 breakfast

unit thirteen

1 1 ✓
   2 ✓
   3 ✗
   4 ✓
   5 ✗
   6 ✗
   7 ✗
   8 ✓

2 1 might
   2 is going to
   3 is going to
   4 is going to
   5 might

say it! *students' own answers*

3 1 What are you doing tomorrow?
   2 What are you doing the day after tomorrow?
   3 What are you doing this Friday?
   4 What are you doing at the weekend?
   5 What are you doing next Monday?

say it! *students' own answers*

4 1 d
   2 h
   3 g
   4 i
   5 b
   6 e
   7 a
   8 c

5 1 Do you ever go to the cinema in the afternoon?
   2 Do you ever watch action films?
   3 Does she ever read horror stories?
   4 Do they ever travel by taxi?
   5 Does he ever watch cartoons?

6 1 romantic
   2 musical
   3 war
   4 thriller
   5 western
   6 cartoon
   7 action
   8 horror

```
R O M A N T I C  H A B
N M U Y C Z X A  S C A
C I S D T T R R  C T B
O K I A X H L T  F I N
M E C P L R L O  H O H
E L A Q O I L N  N N O
D L L Q L L P N  N H R
Y O A E L L T L  W G R
C P T R T E H X  A J O
W E S T E R N A  R O R
```

say it! *students' own answers*

7 1 I'm a bit busy
   2 what are you doing …
   3 Do you want …
   4 What's on?
   5 What's it about?
   6 Where's it on?
   7 Would you like to …
   8 Shall I buy …

responses Sorry, I'm a bit busy tonight.   Yeah, OK. Yes, great. Good idea.

write it! *students' own answers*

8 1 e
   2 a
   3 f
   4 b
   5 c

9 1 b
   2 a
   3 e
   4 f
   5 d

unit fourteen

1 & **say it!** *students' own answers*

2 1 ✓
   2 ✓
   3 ✗
   4 ✗
   5 ✗

write it! *students' own answers*

3 1 have
   2 did you go
   3 Have you ever been?
   4 went
   5 didn't go
   6 didn't have
   7 did you stay
   8 stayed
   9 Did you do …
   10 did

4 1 well
   2 pass
   3 remember
   4 start
   5 lose
   6 badly
   7 win
   8 finish
   9 forget
   10 fail

5 1 well / badly
   2 pass / fail
   3 remember / forget
   4 start / finish
   5 lose / win

6 1 sad
   2 excited
   3 surprised
   4 embarrassed
   5 nervous

7 2 b
   3 c
   4 a
   5 c
   6 b

say it! *students' own answers*

8 1 have a great time
   2 Have a lovely holiday!
   3 Have a nice evening.
   4 Have a good weekend.
   5 Have a lovely day.

9 1 I've run a marathon.
   2 I've visited Italy twice.
   3 I've neve(r) lived alone.
   4 I've been in hospital several times.
   5 I've neve(r) met anyone famous.
   6 I've driven a Ferrari.
   7 I've written a book.
   8 I've learned a lot of English.

say it! *students' own answers*

OXFORD
UNIVERSITY PRESS

Great Clarendon Street, Oxford OX2 6DP

Oxford University Press is a department of the University of Oxford.
It furthers the University's objective of excellence in research, scholarship,
and education by publishing worldwide in

Oxford New York

Auckland Cape Town Dar es Salaam Hong Kong Karachi
Kuala Lumpur Madrid Melbourne Mexico City Nairobi
New Delhi Shanghai Taipei Toronto

With offices in

Argentina Austria Brazil Chile Czech Republic France Greece
Guatemala Hungary Italy Japan Poland Portugal Singapore
South Korea Switzerland Thailand Turkey Ukraine Vietnam

OXFORD and OXFORD ENGLISH are registered trade marks of
Oxford University Press in the UK and in certain other countries

ISBN: 978 0 19 438853 5

Printed and bound in China

ACKNOWLEDGEMENTS

Edited by: Theresa Clementson

Designed by: Bryony Newhouse

Although every effort has been made to trace and contact copyright holders
before publication, this has not been possible in some cases. We apologize for
any apparent infringement of copyright and if notified, the publisher will be
pleased to rectify any errors or omissions at the earliest opportunity.

Illustrations by: Mark Duffin pp.18, 44; Martina Farrow pp.15, 20 (washing etc),
33; Joy Gosney pp.5 (objects), 16 (clocks), 20 (clocks), 25, 26, 28, 57; Joanna
Kerr pp.9, 11, 30, 35, 48, 61; Paul Oakley pp.16 (people), 56; Gavin Reece pp.4,
5 (jobs), 12, 13, 17, 43, 51 (girl and dancer), 60; Three in a Box / Kveta p.39;
The Organisation / Fred Van Delene p.41; Anna Goodson Management /
Mathew Vincent pp.28 (restaurant), 36, 53; Philip Warner pp.8, 10, 20 (get up
etc), 50, 51(aches), 62, 71

*The Publishers and Author would like to thank the following for their kind permission to
reproduce photographs and other copyright material*: Alamy pp.23 (flats), 57 (David
Wall), 64 (Joe); Allstar & Sportsphoto p.34; Empics p.69; Jonathan Fletcher
pp.7 (can, carton); Getty Images pp.14 (Joos Mind / couple, Seymour Hewitt /
family), 19 (Chad Ehlers / city), 21 (John W Banagan), 22 (Peter Cade)
23 (Patrick Molnar / Belinda), 24 (Chris Everard), 32 (Britt Erlanson),
40 (Antonio Mo), 43 (Catherine Ledner / Natasha, Marcus Mok / Cherry),
44 (Ty Allison), 46 (Marvin E Newman), 58 (Will & Deni McIntyre), 59 (Justin
Pumfrey), 63 (Shaun Egan), 68 (Greg Pease); Impact Photos p.37; Istockphoto
p.7 (mug, bottle, glass, coffee cup); Network Photographers p.54 (Peter
Jordan); Oxford University Press pp.7 (couple), 17, 19 (girl), 23 (Bob and
Jamie), 29, 31, 38, 43 (Geoff), 49, 55, 64 (Sally); Rex Features pp.64 (salsa), 67;
Science Photo Library p.6